Is this me?
Am I her?

THE PATH I WALKED

Thank you for Being a supported friend

PAMELA JAMES COLEMAN

EDITED BY VICTORIA HICKS

S.H.E. PUBLISHING, LLC

Is this me? Am I her?
Copyright © 2021 by Pamela Coleman.

This book is a work of fiction. Names, characters, businesses, organiza- tions, places, events and incidents either are the product of the author's imagination or are used fictitiously. Any resemblance to actual persons, living or dead, events, or locales is entirely coincidental.

For information contact: www.shepublishingllc.com

Cover and Title Page Design by Michelle Phillips of CHELLD3 3D VISUALIZATION AND DESIGN

ISBN: 978-1-953163-32-5

First Edition: December 2021

10 9 8 7 6 5 4 3 2 1

This book is dedicated to my father, Alfred W. James Sr., the first man I ever truly loved and who loved me unconditionally. Thank you for being my best friend and protector.

FOREWORD

THERE COMES A TIME when there is so much that could be said, but there is nowhere to start because you have seemingly lost a sense of self.

Is this me? Am I her? The Path I Walked, by the unknown author, Pamela James Coleman, will be hard to put down!

Pamela James Coleman is going to let you in to be embraced by the secret things of the heart that no one talks about, because that's not what we do! We hold it in living inside our heads and wonder why our health fails, and our relationships don't work. We lose ourselves trying to appear perfect.

Is this me? Am I her? The Path I Walked | get ready for the ride! Delve inside and give yourself the right to laugh, cry,

holler, but most of all, think!

-A. Coleman Snead

CONTENTS

INTRODUCTION

I SURVIVED! ALL THOSE NIGHTS, I never thought I would make it to this point. I am free to live, to love, and to enjoy life. After mental abuse, drinking, lies, and secrets, here I am, a woman in her 50s who has gone through a lot. Never did I think I would sit down and tell anyone about all that I went through while growing into adulthood. There is this saying that *"When you get older, you realize that your mother was right."* In my case, that was not true; nothing she said or did would bring me to that revelation. As a child, you should never have to witness drugs, drinking, family secrets, lies, fighting, or mental abuse. How you live or how you were raised, can shape your life. You are led to believe that this is what your life should be. Or is it?

Can you break free from the mold you were raised in? Can you leave the pain behind? To find forgiveness or goodness in the drama that you walked though? Can you?

How hard it is to follow the verse *"Honor thy Mother and thy Father"* when what you feel in your heart to run away from home every chance you get?

CHAPTER 1

SEPTEMBER 27TH—the day that I was born. As an infant, I wasn't told much about what happened. Everything I know to be true about my birth and infancy, I learned from whispers and pictures. I saw photos of me as a baby; my brother was always there beside me in all those photos. My brother and I were 11 years apart, but he always looked out for me. However, my love for my brother can't erase the negative memories associated with my baby picture. I always remember hearing that I was the

New Year's party accident. For a long time, I had no idea what that meant; it was one of those adults' under-the-table jokes. I heard how my mother told the nurses that they had brought in the wrong baby, because her child wasn't that "white". She continued to tell them that I wasn't hers. My dad said, "Look at her hair, she is ours." I had a little black Afro; I think that was the only thing that saved me. So was I an issue from the start? Apparently, I wasn't planned, and I wasn't wanted. Was I a problem from birth?

I was born to, let's just say "Mom and Dad". Dad was a retired Army man and my biggest protector. Unfortunately, Dad was usually protecting me from my mother.

Every child wishes for that happy life that you see on TV; mine was totally different. Not always bad, but not always good. I was brought home to Page Street, a little bungalow, one level, grey trimmed in white. It had two bedrooms, a kitchenette and a living room. Growing up, I was always protected by my dad and my brother. I didn't know what evil and hell lurked ahead of me; for a while, I was protected from it.

I remember always being at my Grandmother's house when I was three or four years old. I have two grandmas, but this one is "Big Granny", my maternal grandmother. Like many African Americans, who worked domestically at times, she was a maid; it was a way of life. I would go with her to work every day, which was always so much fun. I would get a dust cloth and clean all the low areas so that Big Granny, as I called her, would not have to bend over to reach them. I would also get to take the dogs out, which were bigger than me, but I didn't care. I was having the time of my life.

As I got older and a little bigger, the family that my Grandmother worked for, eventually hired me. I got to work just like everyone else. I would go down the barn twice a day and help feed the horses; my favorite was having to feed the 21 cats and kittens. My work clothes that were given to me were like those who rode horses. I had the brown pants and hip boots that you could hear all over the house, clippty-clop, clippty-clop.

I learned so many things while I was living there; out of all of them, I think that it was shared by the employer and my Big Granny, just how to make syrup fresh from a tree. Every morning on the way to work, I would run to see if we had enough sap in the bucket to make the syrup. Who would have thought that putting a hole in a tree to gather sap could be so much fun? Once the bucket was full, my Grandmother would show me how to make it. Once it was gathered, you would have to boil it down to get to the sap part of the syrup. You had to collect a lot of sap to get enough to go on everyone's pancakes, but it was worth the wait and really good.

I also learned how to make quilts from scraps of material. I was too young to use a sewing machine, but I was allowed to put the scraps together, after which my Grandmother would sew them together. One time, she let me put together pieces of my choice as big as I wanted and that was to be my blanket. What fun I had picking my pieces. What I enjoyed about this was, you never had a perfect square. Now, I can make syrup from a tree, I can make a blanket, and she even taught me how to crochet. I was soon making coasters for everyone I knew. Then she showed me how to take my coaster squares and sew them together, to get a throw of any colors or pattern that I wanted.

Our employer's son was a lawyer. Her assistant was one of the nicest people I had ever met as such, I enjoyed hanging out in his office. When I was done with my house chores, her assistant would let me come into her office to play with my toys. I would listen to how he would return calls, as well as observe his typing skills. I thought that was only for women; to top it off, he was black. When he would leave the office, I would sit in the chair like I was typing. Whenever he came back, I would think I was in trouble. Nope, just the opposite.

He said "I have some filing to do, would you like to type?"

"Heck yeah!" I screamed inwardly, as my head bobbed up and down.

He put a piece of paper in the machine and off I went 'peck peck'; I couldn't spell too many words, but I was typing. He was a kind person. I thought he reminded me of my dad, always making sure that I was ok and protected.

Staying there was great. On the days we were not working, I would lay out in the yard and stare up to the clouds for the longest time. I knew that I could touch them and no one could tell me any different. When it was time to go inside, I got to help Big Granny cook dinner. It wasn't fancy, but it was good and it was ours. My favorite food that we would make together would be the potato cakes, made from left-over mashed potatoes that she would fry up in butter with green beans. Oh, my goodness, she could take scraps and make the best dinner ever. She was also famous, in my book, for making breakfast for dinner. When we had pancakes, I got to use the syrup that I had made with the sap from the tree.

In the afternoons, we would sit around and watch TV. Back then, we didn't have a remote control; the TV showed black and white and had three channels with an antenna. If something came on that I didn't want to watch, I would play with my dolls or in a cardboard box. Boxes were my favorite, as when playing with them, you can be anything you want to be and escape the world. Little did I know I would need many boxes growing up, to escape upcoming life events.

One day when Big Granny and I got to work, there was a surprise for me. Our employers got me a goat. Nope, not a puppy, but a goat; it was so much fun raising him and I treated him just like a dog.

When he was little, he was just like any of the other animals that they had on the farm. He would follow me around like a dog and I could teach him to sit or any of the other things that dogs do. He was the coolest pet I could have. We had a hard time naming him, so he got the all-American name, "Billy". Get it? Billy Goat. As Billy started to grow and become an adult goat, he was the size of a puppy, who had the colors grey and white, as well as loved to jump and play. His hard hooves hurt sometimes, but he was always fun.

I soon became worried; most times, he was tied to an iron pole. As he got older, and started growing in his horns, he started butting it. After some time, his head started to bleed, which caused me to worry. I asked if we could chain him to a tree to help with his bleeding. Mrs. Anderson said that Billy would butt anything that is close to him, it's his nature.

One day, after his horns had fully developed, I was feeding him; we were playing as usual. I turned to fill his water pan and he butted me about 3 feet from where he was. It seemed like all play, but the owners and my Grandmother thought it was time for Billy to go to a place where he could be with goats and have fun. I begged them to let him stay, defending that he was playing. They said "No, he must go to a farm, with other animals, so he can run and jump with little goats like himself." This was my first experience of what pain felt like.

My dad would come out on the weekends to bring me fresh clothes and to see my grandparents (his parents-in-law). I would ask where my brother was and he would come out to see me also, but there was someone missing; yes, it was my mother. I would ask and I would always get the same answer, "She is ok, you will see her soon." I had no idea what would await me when I would see my mother soon.

It is the first day of Kindergarten; I was dressed and ready to go, excited as most little kids are when they're ready to do something new. Cute pink dress, sneakers and a backpack bigger than I was. As I waited to go to school, a car pulled up; it was my brother. I was excited I got to ride with him in his cool car. His car was white, with shiny door handles. When he started it up, it sounded like a race car. My first day of school was amazing. We didn't do much, but to me, I had fun, ate lunch and played outside. My brother picked me up from school and back to granny's I went. Pick-up and drop-off was our time to spend together, just to laugh and talk.

One day when school was over, I waited outside for my brother to pick me up, but he was not there; instead, there was someone else there waiting for me—my mother. I wasn't sure if I should be happy to see her, or scared to death. So, I skipped over to her, she was nice to me. For the first time, we walked to our house.

On the walk, I talked about my day. I was hoping to get a snack when I got home, but there was nothing. My mom went to sleep and I went to my room. In my mind, I said, *'This is nothing like being at my Grandmother's, there was always a snack waiting for me.'* There were times that I would get a leftover potato cake. That really made my day.

Soon, I would find out what I was being protected from...

My dad bought a new house, up the street two or three blocks to a white stucco house. It was trimmed in green and had a wooden porch the color of the bricks my daddy worked with. The yard had plenty of room for me to play, even with the huge weeping willow tree in the front. I was most excited about the white picket fence because I thought it meant we were going to be one of those traditional, loving families you see on TV. Boy, was I wrong. My mother got mad at me so many times that I renamed our tree the Whipping Willow.

From the new house, we could hear the horn from the milk plant close by. It would go off twice a day: once at noon and again at five o'clock. My dad got off at 5 p.m. too, so when the second horn went off, I knew it was time for my dad to come home. One day in particular, I started getting excited to see my dad (like always); my mom was still sleeping (also common). My dad came through the door looking for my mother. I heard him call out to her and there was no answer. He called again and I could feel it in the air. It was like a cold chill came over my body. I heard my mother take a deep breath, then it began. "What the hell do you want!?" she growled. *This frightened me, because I had never heard anyone with a tone or voice like this.*

"Is Pooh ready to go?" my dad asked. My mother refused to respond, then I heard footsteps coming towards my room...

"Hello, Pooh" *Phew. It was Dad.* "Are you ready to go to Big Granny's?" he asked. I plopped on the bed and had barely gotten my bag in my hands before I heard yelling from my parents' bedroom. Something about my dad not going to take me anywhere and her wanting me to stay there. *No. way.* I ran to the car, and got in. You could hear the screaming from the house all the way to the car.

"I'm sorry you had to see that. Your mother is not well," my dad said when he finally made it out of the house.

"Whatever. Just get me out of here—and fast!" I thought to myself. "It's okay," is all that came out.

I finally got to Big Granny's. I told her what had happened and that I was scared, because I had never seen or heard people yell like that. She assured me that it was going to get better, I just needed to believe in the Lord. *Ok, if you say so.*

I had to believe, living in the house with my grandparents. My grandfather was the Deacon of the church, so as his granddaughter, you had to be good, which was hard for me, because I never like to sit still. I was always crawling under the pews during church service and getting into stuff. That landed me a spot on the church choir with my Grandmother so that she could keep up with me and I wouldn't get into trouble. Well, that lasted a while. I was out front singing like I was Whitney Houston, but I wished I could have stayed in the background and mumbled the words. Now, they have me in the youth choir and I had to sing every other Sunday. That's what happens when you are a show off.

I would always get to the church and have to go to the bathroom. At that time, there was no indoor plumbing. The church had what you called an "out house". There was a twenty-foot hole dug in the ground with a wooden house on top of it. I was really scared to go into it, because my friend at the church said that people fell into the poop shack and they were never able to get them out, and if I used it, they would reach up and pull me in. In my mind, *it was outside... we were in the country so why not?* I went around the wooden house and went to the bathroom. It was ok, until my Grandmother saw me through the church window coming from the back; I was glad we were on church grounds, no telling what she would have done otherwise.

On the ride back home, I found out what she would have done. Let's just say it was hard for me to sit down once we got home. She explained to me that young ladies do not go outside, pull up their pretty little dresses to use the restroom. She also said, "The stories told to you about people in the bottom, is kids picking on you. No one has fallen into those potties." I wanted to believe her, but it's hard to do so when you look down there and you can't see the bottom.

Sunday afternoons then bring a certain type of fear in me, even more so than getting in trouble a second time for going #1 or #2 at church. I was terrified, knowing I had to go to school the next day. Being picked up by my mother was a fear I couldn't stand. This Monday wasn't any different than the last few, I went to my room, Mom went to the kitchen and turned on the music extremely loud. When Mom would get upset, she would go into the kitchen and turn the music up so no one would talk to her. The five o'clock whistle went off and the knots in my stomach began to ball up. The door opened and Dad stopped by my room to ask if I was ready to go, and that's when it began... "Can you turn down the music a little bit so I can talk to you?" Dad said.

"I don't need to do shit," she replied.

"I would like to tell you where I am going so you will know," he explained.

"You don't need to tell me anything, you are going to do what you want with her so why bother telling me anything?" she argued right back. The music was turned back up. As my dad and I were heading towards the door, something flew by us. My dad pushed me out the door and he was right on my heels. Once we got in the car, I looked back and there stood my mother on the porch yelling bad words, shaking her fist; she told my dad not to bring me back until I was ready to stay.

From that point on, my brother would pick me up, or I would walk home with my cousins on my mother's side and my school friends, to my Aunt's house. I felt like a big kid, because I was walking home. It was a fun time for me, because I didn't have to deal with yelling and screaming every day. I did my homework and played in the backyard; it was great. My dad would be there right after the big horn would go off and take me back to my Big Granny's house. When my dad couldn't do it, my brother would pick me up after he finished working. I finished my Kindergarten year with my brother primarily now taking me to school, picking me up and taking me back to my grandparents.

Summer is here, I knew that I would get to spend the summer with the horses, cats and all other animals I had collected. My dad said, "Let's give Big Granny some rest." Let's go see your other Grandmother. *Oh, NO!* Off I went to my Little Granny, a nickname I gave her because she was short. I was not too excited about going because of what I was leaving behind. At Little Granny's, I didn't have the horses, cats and my Big Granny's cooking.

When I got there, it was something totally different.

At Dad's mom, she didn't have the farm and the animals, but what they had was a swing set for me and a garden to help work in. There were flowers everywhere that I took care of, and weekly trips to the grocery store where I had $2.00 to get what I wanted. Life was good; I always got two comic books and a small toy of some sort to add to a box I had decorated to put my toys in.

There I learned how to cook. My Little Granny was famous for her yeast rolls. My dad always talked about them; she made some for the church every Sunday, and, if someone called, she would make them for any type of event. Again, the fun part about being there was learning how to cook. I had my own easy bake oven. If any of you don't know about the easy bake, it had a light bulb to cook with, so I had these itty-bitty rolls in a little pan that took an hour to cook. Grandpa Rock was my tester; even when I would burn them, he ate all of them, and was proud of me. I never knew how he could eat those hard biscuits, with one tooth on the top and one on the bottom.

Throughout the summer, each day I would wake up, eat a great breakfast and go outside to check all of the flowers that I had planted to see if any needed water. I would take my bucket to the garden and pull all the veggies that were ready to eat. My favorite was the large tomatoes that I picked. I didn't wait for lunch; I would give them to my granny and ask her to make me a tomato sandwich. They were the best.

I was having a great summer, better than I ever thought it would be, the weekend before school started, we would go get school clothes and supplies. My dad sat me down and my heart sank; fear came over me like a thunderstorm. He said, "Your mom seems to be getting better, her tantrums seem to be less. We would like to have her pick you up again from school in the afternoons." *Oh, my goodness I have to return to this hell again.* That dreadful day came; it was time for my dad to pick me up and return me to Big Granny, my other Grandmother.

Elementary School

was heading into the 1st grade, excited to see my friends and to just do something different during the day. our teachers told us to get our bags ready to go; my nerves kicked in. It was time for the bell to ring, it was time for HER to pick me up at the playground. It was time for the drama I live to start. I didn't know why she was picking me up again, I was scared to death. I later learned that my brother's work schedule had changed; she is now picking me up. As we were walking home, she said that I was too small to walk with the big kids. Most of them were in the 5th grade and she thought they would run off, then I would be alone.

When she called my name, I went over and thought I would try something different. I tried to seem happy to see her and tell her all about my first day. I almost passed out, because she seemed different; she was nice, she gave me a hug, listened and laughed at the stuff I told her. Could it be that during the summer she changed?

We stopped by the store on the way home and I got a treat, while she grabbed a few things. I didn't know if I was dreaming or if SHE really changed. Our walk home continued. When we got home, I went to my room, which had been cleaned, with new bed stuff. I was getting so excited that I jumped on the bed. She started cooking dinner and I could smell it in my room. I couldn't wait to see what it was. Daddy came home and asked if I was ready to go; I asked could I eat dinner then go. He said that was ok.

We sat down as a family to eat and I was thinking, *this is great, this is how we are supposed to be.* We were missing my brother, but he was working hard at a major grocery chain. He was positioning to be big one day. Everything was going well at dinner and then it happened. Dad made a comment about something she cooked; my drama was about to start. I knew I was sitting across from the Incredible Hulk! I heard a growl and then it started. My dad sent me to my room and asked me to shut the door. I was crushed. I knew things had changed but they really didn't. *Will she ever change? Will she ever be the mom that I wanted and needed?* I was too young to know and too young to understand.

As time went on, it was the same routine every day; nothing changed. Something was always wrong; my mom never found the middle of the road with her mood swings. It's now

Thanksgiving break. I couldn't wait to go to my little Grandmother for dinner; she cooks the best food ever. There was a large group that always gathered at my Little Granny's, I believe it was because of her cooking. My job for all holidays and Sunday Dinners was to set the table and pour drinks for everyone. I was working hard in the dining room, getting everything just right. There was laughter, storytelling and pictures being shared like you see on TV. I was a happy child, but that didn't last long…

On the ride back home, the yelling and the arguing began between my mom and dad. My brother just pulled me next to him and told me everything was going to be ok.

I trusted my brother; when my dad wasn't around, he would make sure that I was safe. I liked that, because you never know with my mother, when things are going to pop off. I hoped that when we all had Christmas together, she could act like a normal mom for once.

Christmas came at another great time of the year; it is my favorite time of the year. I never could figure out for the life of me, why my dad waited until the 24th to get our tree. We would go through the woods, near my little granny's to pick a tree. Before our search began, he would always tell us to look for one the same height as your mother and as round as she is. I always chuckled at that because my mom was very chunky and maybe 5'2". When we got the tree home, Dad would always put the lights on the tree. I never touched the lights; I got to put all of the decorations on. While I was doing that, Dad went off to read his daily paper, as Mom drank some type of adult Christmas beverage. She was very happy. I think it was the adult drink that did it.

Christmas was good. We all got up and had a good time. My brother was there for a little bit; his birthday is on Christmas Eve, so he would celebrate Christmas Eve night. This made it hard to wake him up on Christmas morning.

Christmas that year I got toys and clothes. My favorite was my Raggedy Anne Doll. As Christmas break drew close to an end, I had my suitcase packed, ready to head to my Grandmother;

that's when the bomb dropped. I was not returning to my Grandmother. I was to stay at home from that point on.

I started to cry because now I would be living the drama every day. I went back into my room and threw my clothes all over the room; it was the largest temper tantrum known to man.

Every night for the rest of the school year, you could hear my parents in a low roar, fussing about something. I wasn't sure what the problem was, I just wanted dad to divorce her so we could leave. I never ever understood why he stayed there and put up with the yelling and cussing every other day, but I would soon find out.

The death of a friend

My mother was not the normal housewife that cooked, cleaned and washed clothes. My dad cleaned and did the laundry. He would go on Sundays, his only day off; this trip, we all went because he had a lot and wanted my mother to help while he went to his part-time job for a little bit. This place was rather large; there was a group of kids playing while their parents washed clothes.

I was looking at the washer that my dad had put clothes in; I saw something red and white rolling around in there. I wasn't sure, but it looked like my Raggedy Anne doll. I moved in closer, it was her. I began to scream, and cry. I was yelling that she is drowning, I tried to pull the door open to get her out; that's when I felt my feet leave the ground, then my bottom was on fire.

Just as she was going to raise her hand again, my dad grabbed her hand in mid-air. I took off and ran to the car as fast as I could. When she got into the car, I laid on the floorboard of the backseat. I learned this trick; her arms can't reach me when I am down there. It didn't save me when I got home. She hopped out the car, pulled me by my feet out the door, and began to wail on me. I guess I was screaming rather loud; the next thing I knew, I had neighbors outside.

I got up and ran into the house. I looked for my brother he was nowhere to be found. I went to my room for safety, I could hear my dad talking to my mother asking her to calm down.

This is when I did nothing but think of how to get out here. *Where could I run to? How long would it take me to walk 12 miles to my Grandmother's house? Would I get kidnapped, killed or eaten by a wild animal? I need someone to get me out, I can't take any more. I am only 8. Someone will come get me so I can live.*

I couldn't wait for summer to come so that I could go see my Grandmother. I didn't care which one. *Just get me out of here. Please!*

Fast-forward to summer, the school bell rang; my bags were packed. I got to spend this summer with my little granny. I now loved going down there, cooking, cleaning and learning new things to cook. It was a kid's summer. There was something about being there, I wasn't looking over my shoulders all the time. I was able to sleep through the entire night; it was the best three months of the year every year.

Then that famous Sunday came, my bags were packed, time for my parents to pick me up. Tucked inside my suitcase was this little teddy bear with bib overalls. My Grandmother told me whenever I was scared to hold the bunny tight and know she was with me.

Going into the second grade, I had Ms. Johnson as my teacher. I felt good going to school, almost safe, because she knew my parents and what was going on at home. It was like having protection at school. It was a normal school day; my favorite part of the school day was recess. I got to see my friends, along with my cousins, even though we were all in different classes and grades. Getting to see them made recess a good part of the day.

Most of all, I would get to have some one-on-one time with Ms. Johnson, during which I could talk to her about what was going on at home. She would always tell me that things would be ok. She said that I needed to trust that my dad was doing all he could to keep me from the things happening at my home. I don't know what I would have done without Ms. Johnson. I really liked going to school. If there was something I was struggling with, she would help me. My mother wasn't much of the 'I will help you with your homework' type of person. Having Ms. Johnson was so nice. That year, when we were getting ready to leave for summer, it was the year I cried so hard, I didn't want to leave Ms. Johnson. I even asked if she could take me home with her for the summer. She gave a little chuckle and said, "What do you do every summer that you love so much?"

I stopped for a minute and a smile came over my face. I yelled, "At my Grandmothers!" She replied, "That is Correct. You see them, you will be outside all the time, cooking fun meals, just enjoying yourself. I will be here when you get back next school year. You can come see me anytime." When she said that, I was very happy. I went home, packed my bags, and waited for the big horn to blow.

Things started to change; what was normal to me was starting to take a shift; it was slow, but I saw it. I would go to my Big Granny's during the week, but when Friday came, I would head to my other Grandmother's home. I knew something was going on. Growing up at my house, you know not to ask questions.

With all of the back and forth traveling, I noticed that I was missing my pink room, not all the fights or drinking back home, but my room. My dad let me go to the paint store with him; I picked out pink, with white flowers and wallpaper. When I returned to my Big Granny's house, I noticed that my grandfather was changing. Nothing big, just that he was moving slower and staying in the bed a lot more.

I was happy to be back; I wanted to feed the cats and horses, as well as play outside; it was so much fun. I soon got some really good news. The Anderson's told me that I would learn how to ride a horse this year, now that I have grown a bit. I couldn't contain my excitement. Mrs. Anderson said on the warm evenings, the horse caretakers would teach me for an hour a day. This is when I said 'I am going to be a veterinarian'.

Lo and behold, my excitement was spoiled, by none other than my mother. *Surprise, surprise.* She called Anderson and she embarrassed me and my Grandmother. She told them that they didn't have a right or permission to let me get on a horse. No matter what my dad might have told them, she was still my mother and she had say-so on if I was to get on such a large animal. Mrs. Anderson told her that she wasn't stable enough to call her house and demand her to do something and, unless she heard it from my father, her request would fall on deaf ears. My mother was in a rage at this point.

When we got home, my grandfather said that my mom called to cuss him out and that she was going to find a way out there to bring me back home and I would never see them again. At that point, I lost it. I started to cry; I couldn't stop. I couldn't understand why she wanted to make my life a living hell. They had to call my dad out there to talk to me. I was assured that as long as she seemed to not be in control of herself, that they wouldn't have me anywhere near her.

My tears lifted, I was calm and wanted to go ride the horses. That now seemed to be the place I would find peace from my crazy life. Summer came and I asked if I could spend the weekends at Big Granny's since I am now learning how to ride my horse; I didn't want to forget what I had learned. My other grandparents would drop me off on Fridays, then Sunday evening, both mom and dad would pick me up. My mom knew that if she wanted to get to know me, she would have to spend time with me. Sundays became our routine dinners at my Little Grandmother's house. They were good; sometimes my mom would get an attitude about something, but there was no yelling at Little Granny's house.

This was the best summer so far. I now have a horse to call my own. I can't wait to tell everyone when I get back to school.

Summer was coming to an end without any major issues and I was looking forward to going into the 3rd grade. I was happy, it seemed like things were going well. Would my life finally be normal like what you see on TV? I wouldn't bet money on it.

Third grade is going to be different; this year I have a male teacher, Mr. Wood. I didn't know what men taught. I always thought they were the principal, the ones that called your parents when you got into trouble. This should be interesting. I couldn't believe how nice he was. He made learning fun! Always looking for ways for us to sing our work.

Because he wanted us to meet new people, Mr. Wood wouldn't let us sit with our friends; that wasn't so nice of him. With what I have going on at home, I really didn't want to meet new people, I didn't want them to know what I go through every day. I feared that they would make fun of me or tell someone. I didn't think that telling anyone would matter, as often as the police came to the house. They already knew what was going on.

For my birthday, my brother had got me a set of headphones. He said this would help drown out the arguing while I was trying to go to sleep; he was correct, I didn't hear a thing, it was so much easier to go to sleep. It was the first time I ever slept through the night at my own home.

One weekend, Big Granny called to see if I could spend the week down there with them. I was so excited, I knew that I was going to have a great week, oh was I wrong. My Grandmother's sister was from Rhode Island. She was ok but super strict up north; they are harder on kids because it's mainly a city and they are harder on their kids than the people in the country.

I noticed that my grandfather wasn't as cheerful or picking on me as usual, he was staying in bed, coughing a lot and breathing heavily. Towards the end of the week, I was not allowed to go back into the room where he was. That Sunday, my Grandmother looked very upset and her eyes were full of tears.

I asked her if she was ok. She said, "No, your Papa, just died." I wasn't sure what she meant by that. I knew goldfish die, cats and dogs die but not my grandfather. She kept me in my aunt's bedroom and told me to stay in there with her while my Aunt took care of things out there.

My big mistake was looking out the window. There was a black station wagon like car, then two men with a bed on wheels were pushing it with a large black bag. I asked my Grandmother what was in that bag, she said, "Your grandfather." I started to scream and cry. Why did they have him in a bag? "He can't breathe in there! Open it up!!" I yelled, as I kept banging on the window for them to stop. They kept pushing him to the car. I was mad at the men for not listening.

A week went by and I was soon dressed in a cute black dress. We were at the church, but where was my grandfather? This is his church. *Why is he not standing in line with the rest of us?* The music started to play and we all walked in the church two by two. I could see at the front there was this long box, I wondered what was in it and why it was here.

As we got closer, I looked in, *OH MY GOD,* there was my grandfather lying very still and not talking. So, I asked my brother why was Papa laying there like that. He said, "Pooh (that's what they called me) Papa has died, he has gone to heaven with God, and his mother." That was not good for me to hear; I lost it again, ran over to the box thing and started yelling to 'wake up!' "Wake up!!!! Don't leave me!" I didn't realize my action had the entire church, small as it was, in tears. I just wanted him back, I wanted to see and talk to my giant size grandfather. It was not meant to be. The slow singing and flower-bringing started.

Once it was over, we filed outside again; this time the entire church followed behind us. We walked over to a tent that was set up in the yard with a bunch of stone markers. The box that my grandfather was in, was laid upon these belts. Again, with the singing, something very strange started to happen, the preacher said, "Ashes to ashes, dust to dust," then my grandfather was lowered into the ground. Being a young kid, no one told me about death or funerals. I started to scream that "You can't put him in the ground, he won't be able to breathe! Stop it, stop it now!" Again, my brother was there to help me understand that he was no longer here on earth, that this was just his shell. "Granddad is looking down on us from heaven and protecting us. So, it is ok for the box to go in the ground. It is just a symbol that he is now at rest."

I get it now, but it still hurts that you will no longer see him and sit in his lap and hear the "good ole days" stories, which you knew most of them were tall tales. He was telling me to keep me interested. I wanted to move in with Big Granny so she wouldn't be alone, but her sister was there to keep her company.

When I was alone with my Grandmother, I told her of the fighting, and loud voices that are muffled behind my wall which connects to my parents' room. I told her I don't understand why my mother is like this. *"Is she angry at me? Am I the reason why she acts this way?"* I asked these, among many other things, in a frustrated rant. She told me, "No". She said my mom was really sick and that she was hoping that she gets better.

"Sick?!" I yelled. "She looks fine to me," I said, confused.

"No, Pooh, a different kind of sick," Big Granny responded. She then explained that adults have a strong, special beverage they like to drink that's not for young people. Something about how when they have too many at one time, it makes them act a certain way.

"So, my mom's a drunk?" I blurted out. Big Granny seemed shocked that I knew what a drunk was.

"Something like that," she said after a long pause.

Apparently, my mother has no control over when to stop and she is mixing her doctor's medication with it. Big Granny told me that when she is just taking her medication, she is fine, but when she drinks, she is a totally different person—a person that we don' t care to know. A person that is only thinking of herself. A person that can be dangerous. I had seen glimpses of this person. All of a sudden, I understood why my family didn't want me around her when she was like this.

I sat at the kitchen table for a while, trying to process everything Big Granny had just told me. *Was my mom a drunk and a drug addict? Is that what's wrong with her? But what would make her do this? Why would she not want to take care of her own daughter, like every other mother?* Something that would stay with me.

Everything was a blur after that. Between the death of my Papa, and the partial revelation about my mother, I remember almost nothing about the rest of that year. My mother's drinking picked up after her father's death. The outburst during the summer got worse. I didn't go back home at all. I spent the entire summer with my Big Granny and I saw my other Grandmother on Sundays for our Sunday dinner.

The start of the 4th grade year, I was spending more time with my Big Granny. I didn't want her to be alone since my Papa's death. I know her sister was now living with her, but she hadn't been there with her; she needed a familiar face to help her through. I think that we were helping each other. We would have long talks at the table during my favorite meal, which was dinner. I believe that is when I learned that everyone has a path. Our paths are determined for us when we are born. This will be something that I would always remember to help me get through life.

We really did help each other through a really tough time. My mother would come out on Saturdays to stay overnight; she would just cry and throw fits like the people you see in the church jumping up and down and falling out.

One weekend, my mother thought it would be a good idea to put a perm in my hair. She said when I would come home, it was too much work for her to do my hair. It was very thick and she was tired of dealing with it. I would always complain about how she fixed it. Ok let's have a quick lesson on black people's hair. Our hair is naturally curly, so the perm that you are supposed to put in our hair is a straight perm. Why did my mom put a perm in for white people? First of all, she messed it up, by not following the directions, then my granny was trying to tell her that this was not what she was supposed to put in my hair, she continued. When she was done, I looked like I had just licked an electric plug, better yet, a clown in the circus, with the big puff of hair that wouldn't do anything. I couldn't comb it or style it. II started to cry; my mom then started to yell at me and told me that I was not being grateful. *HOW* could I be grateful knowing that I had to go to school looking like this?

"You have a problem with me putting your hair in the Afro-puffs so I try this to make YOU happy and *this* is how you act?" My mother screamed at me.

"If I knew it was going to be messed up like this, I would have run from you," I yelled back. Big mistake.

The next thing I knew, she had the fly swatter in hand, ready to beat the hell out of me. My granny tried to stop her, but my mom pushed her back. Big Granny wasn't harmed, but the shove was enough to really shake her. Things got ugly fast. My mom began to raise her voice at my Grandmother; she said she didn't need to get in the middle of something that wasn't her problem. With a calm voice, my Grandmother asked her to look at my hair, "This is something that can be fixed. Don't get upset because she didn't like it." My mom was still upset, and it was hard to calm her down.

"It's time to go to the barn to feed the cats and the horses," Big Granny said as she ushered me outside away from my mother. Once your dad gets your mother out of the house, I'll do what I can to fix your hair.

In all that chaos, I guess she had found time to call my dad. He was at the door in less than an hour to take my mom back home. I could hear my parents arguing about my hair. As I walked to the barn, this mess on my head wouldn't fit under a hat. I was crying all the way there.

When we got to the barn, the Andersons were down there with the horse caretakers, along with people with white coats on. Everyone saw me standing there and turned almost at the same time and yelled, "Stop stay there!" I had no idea what was going on but I was soon to find out. Dr. and Mrs. Anderson walked me out of the barn, and told me that my horse, whose name is Tangy, was bitten by something; she had gotten very sick and the doctors had to put her to sleep. I was confused and they could see it. Mrs. Anderson said she will be joining your grandfather.

I then understood what she was talking about. I fell to the ground in tears. Just when I thought that I was done trying to understand death, they were taking my horse, Tangy, away from me too. I thought that the people in the white coats were supposed to *save* animals, not *kill* them. That very moment I changed my mind; if I couldn't take care of the animals anymore, I didn't want to be a veterinarian anymore, I refuse to kill anything.

I left the barn area and you could hear my parents, more mom than dad, still going at it. I walked really slow until I heard mom and dad leave. I got back to the house; my granny saw that I was upset and said, "Don't worry, your mom will be ok." I told her about Tangy, she too was sad about them putting her to sleep. I told my granny that my back was hurting, so she looked at it and there were marks on my back from the whipping. I am not sure what she put on it, but the pain disappeared quickly.

Monday came before I knew it, which meant it was time to go back to school. Despite Big Granny's best efforts, my hair was still a mess from the perm, and my back was still sore and covered in marks from the whipping. I asked my Grandmother if I had to play during recess; she said just sit out and you will be ok. When recess came, I did just that; the teacher started asking questions, why was my back hurting? I didn't know that you were supposed to keep whippings to yourself.

I told my teacher that I made my mother mad about my hair, which kids were picking on me really bad about. So, she took me to the nurse, and saw the wheals on my back. She called my mother; you could hear her yelling on the phone. She explained that I was talking back, and when she went to spank my bottom, I ran away from her and that's how they got there.

What!!! That's not true! You did this! But I didn't say anything, because I knew I would see her again. I didn't know what she would do now with the school calling her. I guess the nurse bought the answer she gave. She put some medicine on my back and sent me back outside.

The rest of the week, the kids would pick on me until my Grandmother finally got my hair fixed or close to normal. She washed my hair every day. She would put them in braids until they could find someone to fix it.

4th grade was a year I just wanted to forget. Bad hair, whippings, my horse died. Now I was really ready for summer to come so that I could go to my other Grandmother's house. I never thought that I would want to get away from my Big Granny's, but living with the reminders of my Papa all around, the barn where my horse used to be, I need to get away. I was not going to go home to that uncomfortable living that my mom made for us on a regular basis.

It finally arrived. I was at the pick-up spot with my friends. At the end of every school year, we would all stand there and cry. This year I didn't have any tears, I was ready to go. I wanted to get away from everything. My brother pulled up to get me and he had my clothes with him. I didn't even have to step one foot into that house. I went straight from school to little granny's house.

Summer was great. I only saw my mom on Sundays for dinner; she didn't dare act a fool at Little Granny's. She would set her straight; I saw her do that once, it was funny. I am not sure why she didn't like my Grandmother. She didn't do anything to her. However, my mom got along with my grandfather; she spent most of her time when she was there talking to him. She never said much to us, which was fine with me. I was still mad that she beat me like she did because I said something about my hair, I still have the marks to prove it.

I was busy during the summer; I worked in the garden and

planted my own tomatoes and potatoes, which caused me to fee

like a farmer. This was fun; I asked my Grandmother if I could try

planting flowers. She said yes, so I got a spot in the yard that was

just mine to work with. It was so pretty, I got a large rock out of

the woods behind the house, made a pretty circle with them and

for a few weeks, I would use my store change to get seeds. I didn't

know what flowers I was getting, but I eventually got the ones

with the pretty pictures on them.

The planting began. While I was waiting for my flowers to grow,

I painted the wooden fence for my grandparents. When I was

done with that, they told me I did such a good job that I could

paint the outside furniture. I was rather excited when they told

me that this would be what I would do every summer.

My flower garden started to come in. It was so colorful, it looked

like a rainbow. When the neighbors would drive by, they would

stop in to see my garden; my grandparents were very proud of

my work. One Sunday, when my parents came out for dinner, I

had made a bunch to give to my mother. She told me how pretty they were and they both expressed how proud they were of me. When it was time for them to go home, my mother left her flowers. I was crushed, to which my Grandmother said, "I am sure she didn't mean to, people forget things."

Nevertheless, that was one of the best summers I had so far. I was busy the entire summer, with all the fun things I was doing. I did miss my Big Granny, and all the animals, but she had her sister with her now, so I didn't worry as much about her.

It was time for school to start, as I prepared to go into the 5th grade, the last year in the elementary school. This was the year that I was picked on, bullied and had to move back to home to the drama, which was almost daily. At the start of this year, I am now home with my parents and brother, trying to be positive, but still scared. I am not sure if I mentioned I have what people call a 4-finger forehead. What is that you say? Put your four fingers together, place it over your forehead; if any of your forehead showed, you were picked on badly. I used to get slapped on the forehead and called names during recess. The only time that this didn't happen was when I put a small amount of hair over my forehead, which is called a bang. When I wore my hair in that style, no one said or did anything to me.

When Sunday arrived, all that would change. Mom would wash my hair; sometimes she would understand what I am going through, other times she didn't give a fart. She would either put my hair in two Mickey Puffs, or that one long braid down the middle of my head. It was pulled so tight that my eyes would squint back. I had a friend at school that I hung out with. He was white and also picked on and called a nerd, because he wore glasses and said he wanted to be a doctor. We hung out together, which somehow resulted in us not getting picked on as much.

One day, when I got home from school, there was loud music coming from the kitchen, along with singing. I went in to speak to my mom and her response was, "Not now, go to your room." I forgot who I was talking to, and responded, "What did I do? I just walked through the door." Oh shit, it hit the fan, I got verbally jumped. Her response was, "I didn't ask for your back talk." I got a beating just for asking a question. Her beatings were not the normal *you are in trouble* type beatings; they always felt like she was taking something out on me and I didn't know what or why.

Soon after, Dad came home. That's when it really hit the fan. Mom went in on Dad, how she had heard some ladies talking about a guy named Sonnie; that is my daddy's nickname with his friends. Mom didn't hear the conversation or what was even said. All she knew was that two women were on the bus talking about him; it was automatic that he was cheating on her. I heard a lot of yelling, then a thump. I looked out the door and daddy was on the floor. I started to scream, then he turned to my mother. "Look what you've done!" Her response was, "I don't really give a shit, this is about you cheating on me."

She went back into the kitchen, threw dinner on the table, grabbed a fifth of gin and went into the living room, before sitting in her favorite chair next to the front door. She yelled back in the kitchen that she better not hear us talking about her. I didn't understand why my dad stayed with her; later in life, I would find out why.

At that point, I began wishing my life away. As the old people would say, I couldn't wait to get to middle school, then to high school, then college and then out of this house of constant drama.

During my fifth-grade year, just about every week to every other week there was something for my parents to argue about. If my mom was having it out with my dad, she was having it out with her sister. Another person that I can't figure out why they continue to stick together, that too will become clear sooner than later.

I was excited about 5th grade; this would be my last year of being picked on and bullied. Like everything, there is always a turn around the corner to mess your happiness up. Our last grade in elementary school was the year to learn about the female body and the male body. *WHAT!? Who said it was ok for us to see other people's private parts?*

I told my mom about this when I got home. She was pretty nice about it; she sat me down and told me that at some point in life, we will have to learn about it, that one day we would see each other naked and it was a part of life. "EW! I don't want to talk about it anymore." My mother said, "Don't worry, you do not have to take this class until after Easter break is over." Easter break got here very fast. I was excited for the week off, as I got to stay with my Little Granny.

Easter for our family was a big thing; we used to attend the Easter Sunrise services. That was a church service that started at 6:00am. Afterwards, we would always have the best breakfast that my Grandmother could fix up.

This year, there was a little drama; we had issues with the dress that I was supposed to wear. Every year, I would get a bright pretty Easter dress. This year, my mother thought it was a good idea to get me this dingy brown dress with an uglier vest to go with it. I sat in my room and cried. I was not going to wear this thing so what was I going to do?

I went into my grandfather's medicine bag, took a straight razor and I cut the dress. My mother blew the roof off the house, saying I cut the dress. My Grandmother said, "How is she going to get a sharp object like that to cut the dress?" She continued by saying "It was probably like that and you just didn't pay attention to it." That didn't make things any better; my mom continued to say I did it, then my dad jumped in and agreed with my Grandmother.

Yes, I did feel bad, but not bad enough to say I did it. My Grandmother took me shopping and I got the cutest, bright dress with hand gloves and a purse. I was the first one up for Easter service; when my mom saw me, she leaned over and whispered "I know you did it, when you get home, I am going to whip your ass when I get you home." At this point, the fear of the almighty was in me.

I don't know who took over my body and my mouth. I turned to her and said, "I didn't do it and you can't prove it. Hit me and I will tell my daddy." *Whap!* I was backhanded in the mouth; it was loud enough for my dad to hear it. He looked at me, and was about to say something, but my Grandmother said, "Let's go to church everyone, we can work this out after the service."

This service, I told my Grandmother that I wanted to sing with the junior choir. Was it me feeling a bit guilty? Who knows? I had an amazing time up there singing. After the service, we went back to my Grandmothers; at that time, my mom said I was a good little singer, and that she was sorry for the way she handled the dress issue.

I did feel better now about going home. Oh, was I wrong; this was far from over. It started in the car with my dad saying to her, "Have you lost your damn mind smacking that child like that?" *OH NO!* She was going to blow! She turned to the side, and said, "I will slap you like that. You keep taking up for this child like she is some type of angel, the more this damn family spoils her, the worse it's going to be."

Before this became a full-blown argument, he said, "I am doing everything I can to make sure that she has a normal and safe life. You act like you didn't want her when she was born, I am going to protect her to the fullest." We couldn't get home fast enough,

I wanted to find my brother and run.

We were barely out of the car, when she swung at him. My daddy ducked the swing, lost his balance and fell to the ground, then she threw her purse at him. I began to scream; my neighbors came out running and took me into the house; the police were there within 5 minutes.

I was screaming from the house to take her away. Again, my dad took up for her, said that everything was going to be ok, after which the police left. For hours, I would plot how to run away; if you opened the back door to the house, it made too much noise, and where would I go? That was my biggest problem, I had nowhere to go.

I used to sleep walk when I was younger; *I wonder if I put a bag of clothes outside behind the tree, would they think I was sleep walking or running away?*

Then I thought *if I ran away, who would protect dad? Who would call the police if the neighbors don't hear them? What if she really flipped out and tried to kill him?* I couldn't leave, I put my runaway bag under my bed, hoping I would never have to use it.

The day came for the class. It was much better that they split us up. It was only girls in the classroom. It was somewhat shocking; there were a lot of sniggles and giggles in the room. When it came time to talk about the boys' parts, one of the girls said, "I have seen that before." The room got quiet; we all looked at her. She said, "I have a brother, why are you guys looking at me?" I am sure we were all thinking the same thing.

I couldn't wait to get out of school that day. I called my Big Granny to tell her what a day I had, and all the stuff that they talked about. Why did my mother get upset that I was talking to her on the phone about my day? I turned to her, "Mom, you both can hear it at the same time. I won't have to repeat myself." I thought that would help, it didn't; she just stop talking to me. I feel like I could never win with her.

We had our 'know your body' class for a few weeks. Every day I was in the class, I would wish for the last day of school. Before you know it, my wish came true. At this point, we had a week left in 5th grade. I couldn't wait. Before school was out, they had to embarrass the entire 5th grade. We all got personal bags; the girls got sanitary items, deodorant and pamphlets to know your body. The boys got soap, deodorant and mouthwash. The boys and the girls teased and picked on each other the entire day, because of what was in our bags.

Finally, I could say "Today is a very happy day because it is the last day of 5th grade." It was good for many reasons; this is where kids are split up based on where they live. The bullies that were picking on me would go to a different middle school. I was going to a middle school, which put me 8 years closer to getting out of the house. The only sad thing was my nerdy friend; his parents said that they were putting him in a private school because of how bad we were picked on. I was left to deal with the bullying alone. The bell rang, a sign that summer was here; time to say our good-byes. Knowing that I wasn't going to see my friend again was tough. We stood in pick-up and cried until his parents picked him up and I walked home.

I no longer go to my Grandmothers for the summer; I can go visit them on the weekend, but I am now staying at home. Some days are good days and then others are hell. I did like the fact that we lived across the street from a park. My friends, and my 1st cousin would spend all the time we could during the summer, going to the park, riding bikes across town and hanging out in each other's house.

I was always on pins and needles when they would come to my house, because I wouldn't know when she would show herself. One day, we were in my room, I didn't see it coming. It was getting close to the start of middle school. We got our schedules, all of us were excited about what classes we got and who we were going to see. Someone said something about boys and having a boyfriend. My mom rolled in my room like the Tasmanian Devil, saying that we don't know anything about boys, that we need to calm down with our fast selves, or next thing you know, we would all end up pregnant. She just went on and on and on, until the girls were embarrassed. The girls eventually left; my mom yelled back to my room that she was going to call all of their parents. I was in my room crying; she laid it to me and said

that if she hears anything else about boys, I would regret it.

Middle School

Elementary school years are now over; I am 7 years away from where I really want to be, out of the house. Now, I am in middle school in the 6th grade. I have grown up and am much more aware of what is going on in life and at home. Now that I am in middle school, I have the drama I live with at home and now peer pressure, as well as a dirty little secret that it seems like everyone knows about, but me.

Our middle school was two times the size of my elementary school. I was nervous and angry. All my friends were coming to school in cute jeans, tops and shoes looking fresh out of a teen magazine. As for me, Mom put me in an ugly little dress, with sandals and when I say ugly, it was U-G-L-Y. It reminded me of the ugly Easter dress she tried to put me in. There were so many new faces that blended in with the old faces, yes really cute boys, but they were all in the 8th grade; none of them would pay any attention to this girl. I was late to every class that day due to how large the school was and I didn't know my way around, so when I walked into the class, everyone was looking at me at some point and laughing because of what I had on. I sat in my chair and almost started to cry. I was back in elementary school, because my mother was projecting her image onto me. This is not fair, but I can't say anything about it, or can I?

When I got home, that familiar smell was coming from the kitchen, one that, at some point in your life you would be tired of smelling it. Yup, fish sticks with pork and beans. I thought *no, I knew my mom could only cook three things, spaghetti, fish sticks which just required heating up and fish cake.* Every meal was served with a side of apple sauce, whether you wanted it or not. This applesauce was made by none other than my Little Grandmother. Now that lady can cook; I couldn't wait to get to her house on Sunday just to see what we were eating. We never missed a Sunday, with or without my mother or my brother.

Lately, things with my brother were starting to change; I didn't know what it was, but you could tell. I went into the kitchen and she was in an ok mood, so what better time to say, "Mom, can I get some different clothes?" She turned slowly towards me; at that very moment, I saw it coming. "Why in the hell do you need new or different clothes?" I felt myself shrinking, wishing I had never opened my mouth. I said, "the other kids in school…" before I finished, all hell broke loose, "I don't give a shit what other kids have or don't have. You have a closet of clothes that you will wear until you outgrow them, don't come back to me with that shit again you hear me?" "Yes, ma'am," I said, but I had a plan. When we go shopping with my Grandmother, I will put clothes in her basket a little at a time. I will tell her what happened with school and Mom. She will help me, she always does.

Going back to school every day, I had gotten used to the laughter and it soon went away, because we all started to get to know each other. They also found out what was happening in my house, then they understood. However, that didn't last long. As the school year went on, something else came into the picture that would give the other students something to pick on me about. Yes, the boyfriend thing. Everyone had a boyfriend but me. You would see them disappear behind the building and come back smiling. Peer pressure is a bitch; I got talked into going behind the building with one of the guys. He said that he was going to act like he did something, and told me to just hang back here for a little bit. *I don't want to be here at all, pretend or not.*

Time was up. He ran from behind the building telling everyone that I stink, that he couldn't do anything with me because I smell like tuna. I ran up the steps nonstop until I got to the nurse's office; she asked what was wrong, I told her. She turned beet red with anger. She said, "I got to call your mother so she can pick you up from school. We will let you stay home for a few days to let this go away." Oh no, "Please don't call my mother, she will..." I stopped quickly. The nurse said, "She will do what?" "Oh, just be mad that's all." The nurse didn't buy what I was saying at all.

When she called my mother, you could hear her screaming on the phone, one about what I did, and two because she had to leave work to get me, which means she would have to get a taxi cab to school in order to take me home. I was shaking when I heard her; the nurse could see the fear on my face. The nurse replied, "Ma'am, you stay at work, I will keep her in here until you and your husband can come get her."

The nurse walked me to my class as we passed the office. I saw some of the guys sitting in there waiting to see the principal. When I walked past them, they called me fishy snitchy. I started to cry all over again; this is the name that stayed with me for weeks. Mom and Dad got to the school around 5:30pm at least 2 hours past the school closing. She explained to them what had happened at that time. Mom was a loving mom, hugging me and telling me it was going to be ok; all show. Dad thanked her, and we left.

The car ride back seemed very closed in and stuffy. You could cut the air with a knife. Not 2 or 3 blocks from that house, Mom turned in slow motion. *Here it comes.* She yelled at me for going back there, for letting other people talk me into that; she said I must have been out of my mind for doing that. She asked what in the hell I was thinking. I must have lost my mind at the school, because I snapped back and said, "If you had listened to me when I came home about the clothes, you would know that I am picked on non-stop. You would know that I was looking forward to going to middle school just to get away from being picked on, only to have it start again because I am wearing dresses all the time, which also makes it easy for the boys to pull my dress up from the back and make fun of me. So, I thought going in the back like the other girls, would cut that out; but I was just set up by the same mean kids that had been picking on me. This will never end."

As we pulled up in front of my house, she hadn't said a word to me after I said what I said. I really thought she was going to knock out my teeth, but instead she said she was sorry, that "tomorrow we will get you some new clothes, ok?" I said, "Thank you." I gave her a hug, she said, "Go lay down and rest while I get dinner ready." I looked at Dad, he had a smile on his face that showed he approved.

It was time for me to return to school. I was nervous, but ready. Mom really listened to me. I got jeans, cute tops, and a new backpack. She kept some of my clothes; the rest we shared with a family in need. She also took me to get my hair fixed. The bus pulled up. I got on the bus, and all you heard was a gasp and as I walked to the back where I like to sit, only one person called me fishy snitchy. So far, I am good.

Here we go, I walked into the school, and no one paid any attention to me; *this is great did it go away like that?* I went to class, where the picking crew sat. They glared at me while I was getting ready to sit down; someone pulled my seat from under me and said, "Welcome back fishy snitchy."

I wanted to cry, but I wasn't going to let them win. I remember what Mom and Dad said when I left the house that morning. "Hold your head up, don't let them see you are upset." I got up off the floor and said "Thanks, I am glad you guys missed me."

They said nothing, then someone said, "We missed that smell, the group erupted in laughter." I said "How could you? I didn't think you could smell anything over those run over sneakers." That was the last time I was called any name other than my birth name.

What? My parents were right? They helped me without fighting, what a good feeling to have. As the school year went along, I was no longer the target, that became someone else. I was actually in the "group", I was shocked. This was my turn to show the group that you don't have to pick on someone to feel important. You could be just the opposite and be bigger. It was time for the talent show, the show that I had no plans on participating in because of all the harassment that I had gone through. That didn't stop the group. I was now part of a singing group because I sang in the church choir. We practiced and had so much fun. Would you believe the new kid that was being picked on was now included, and yes, I got our group to stop being the mean students.

The time had come for the talent show. We had two: one for the school during the day; and one in the evening for the parents. I was so hoping that no one I knew would attend, but no, there was an entire entourage, from my Mom and Dad to Grandparents and Cousins'. I thought I was going to throw up, but I didn't. I stared at the bright spot light so that when I looked out in the crowd, I couldn't see anyone. It worked. The music started. Cherly Lynn *"to be real"*, the song took over me, it was the performance of a lifetime.

I went backstage and was so shocked to see my mother there. She was smiling; she told me how proud she was of me; this was the mom I was missing. Dad dropped us off at home, as he had to go to his part-time job. I said, "Since I was the reason you were late, I can go help you." The air got thick; I could feel the hair on the back of my neck start to move. That's when it happened, "So you don't want to be here at home with me?" my mom barked. I tried to explain that I didn't want Dad to have to be out extra late just because he was there to support me. *Oops wrong thing to say,* "So it's ok for me to be up?" Dad said, "Pooh stay here I got it." My mother's response was, "Oh hell no, I don't need her to stay because you told her, she should want to stay, not because you told her to." This was a long night; my mother didn't let this go; I could hear the muffled argument in the room next to mine.

With all the drama this school year, 6th grade ended with embarrassment, learning lessons, making new friends and how bad peer pressure can be.

Summer was here, time to do nothing but hang out with my cousins, bike riding, cookouts and parties at the park. I couldn't wait. I thought about joining the scouts for the summer, *Nah not this year*. During the summer, one of our school friends moved into the neighborhood. She started to hang out with us and we were all having a good time. I was starting to spend a lot of time with her, hanging out at her house; I also noticed that my other friends, relatives and I had started to drift apart. I was ok with it; she had an older brother that I had a crush on, so for me, this was perfect. I got to see him when I went over and hoped that he would one day notice me. He did notice me, but in all the wrong ways. I was viewed as his sister's friend, so he treated me like a little sister instead of that girl he could walk down the aisle with. My heart was broken or so I thought; when he came home with his girlfriend, then I knew my heart was broken. I would never get a chance with him.

I really started to miss my friends that I hung out with, the fun we would have just doing nothing on some days. Oh, how I longed for that time again. I slowly found myself hanging out with them again, as I moved back towards my family and friends. My mom was starting to hang out with her mom. This was getting awkward; Mom always wanted me to go to hang out with, her, so I sucked it up and went with my mom. Here we go, having to fake being around her; one day all hell broke loose. We were outside sitting on Tasha's front porch when my friends walked by. The group was like, "HEY, what's up guys, want to go with us? We are walking to the store." Tasha replied, "No, we are fine." I told her, "You can't speak for me. Sure, I will go with you all. I want some candy anyway." Tashsa began to yell at me. She said the only reason I was hanging out with her was because of her brother.

I replied that "Your brother ain't all that! I don't know why you are making such a big deal about this." She got angrier. Then she started saying things that I didn't understand so I turned around and yelled, "Say it to my face then!" She ran up the street to me and said, "At least I don't have family secrets!" Well, I thought she was talking about how my mom would go off the deep end, and show herself out in the streets. That's not much of a secret, but ok if you say so.

She grabbed my shoulder, turned me around and said, "You know our swimming teacher at school? I said "Yeah, that is your aunt's son." well that's your brother. Don't ever speak to me again."

I knew she was lying, so I ran back into my house and yelled at my mom to tell me she was telling a lie. My mother grabbed my arm like I had done something wrong and dragged me out the house. She told me, "Don't believe everything you hear." That was the last time we both went to Tasha's house.

That weekend, I asked to go see my Big Granny, which was my mom's mother (or so I thought). When I got there, it was good to be away from the drama that was happening at home. We sat down to some tasty potato cakes, which she knows I love. I started with "Granny, you won't believe what I have been told." She sat still for a moment, then she said, "Go ahead child, let me hear it."

I began to tell her everything that Tasha told me; I told her that she said I had a brother, that he wasn't daddy's. I also told her that when I asked Mom about it, she told me it would be ok. Granny dropped her head like she was saying a prayer, then she looked up at me and said it's true. Klein is your brother, "What? You have to be shitting me!" I yelled. She said, "Yes," and responded again, "Yes, it is."

"Your parents got into an argument and your dad left for a little bit, while he was gone, your mom was seeing someone else, which was the result of your cousin/brother. You mom's sister offered to take him and raise him as her own; that is how this mess has come about. So, the person that you always thought of as your cousin, is your brother." I asked who his father was and she said, "I don't know". Once she said that, this was a dead subject to me. Until my mom tells me he exists, and who his father is, he will remain my cousin.

Now that this has happened, I no longer want to talk to or be around Tasha. The more I thought about it, the madder I got at her. *How dare she say something like that to me? Where did she hear it from and how did they find out? Is this something that everyone in this small town knows about? Was I the only one who didn't, just to protect me? Now my blood is boiling.*

A few weeks later, my friends and I were walking to the store, when we bumped into Tasha. She was all smiles and said, "Happy to see you smile, like nothing hadn't gone down a few weeks ago!!!" So, I played along to see what else she knew, "Hey Girl, want to hang out with us?" I spoke. She agreed, now I can ask all my questions. I started by saying, "Hey Tasha, I am sorry for acting like a jerk a few weeks ago." She replied, "Don't worry about it, water under the bridge." "Thanks, can you tell me how you found out?" I replied. "Sure, I overheard my mom talking to some lady that had come over about how your mom had been with someone other than your dad, and the result was Klein."

"Did they say who the father was?" I pressed. She said, "No". She had stopped listening, the only reason that she said anything to me was just to get back at me, so we moved on.

All that happened over the summer, which made it a little uneasy to return to school. My "brother" works at the middle school now as a swimming teacher. Before I found out all of this information, I had signed up to take swimming classes. I was excited about it, until now! Everyone thought I was going to stick with Gymnastics. I loved it, until that day I was trying to teardrop. I landed on my ass; that was it. Never to do that again.

I went to swim class. When I got there, someone said, "Hey Sis." I spun on my heels, and responded, "You are not my brother. You are my cousin, and until someone tells me differently, that is the way it's going to be. Klein continued to teach class and that was the last time we spoke of this." Then the teasing came, "It's nice to have someone that works in the school to look out for you. You will get an "A" in this class without doing anything." I was pissed; I felt like the way the comments were said, they knew the rumors. I tried to get out of his swimming class, but that didn't work.

The only thing middle school kids are supposed to worry about is pimples, what boy/girl liked them and who to sit with during lunch. Not me, I had to worry about how many people know this dirty little secret.

It felt like I spent the entire 7th grade looking over my shoulder, taking apart everything someone would say to me, to judge if they had any information about this dirty little secret.

I was at home for the summer; it wasn't all bad. It seemed like everyone that I was related to lived on our street and reminder, we also lived across the street from a park. I loved it when we would all get together; this is my mother's side of the family, because my dad was an only child.

There was always a party on our street; if it was at the park or in someone's backyard, everyone knew everyone, and I bet they all knew about this dirty little secret. However, I said that until I heard it from my parents, especially my mother, Klein would remain my cousin.

The music and the food were always good. We would hear stories of when they grew up, which I loved. There was always someone dancing in the yard; that was good to be around. Most of them were closer to my brother than to me because they were all close in age. My brother was eleven years older than I was, but that didn't stop me from hanging out with my cousin and friends that lived on the same street.

We went everywhere together. Our favorite thing was when they had the community parties at the park; everyone would be there, even the people from across the tracks as we like to say. When we would ride our bikes, we would go across the tracks to hang out even though we were not supposed to due to our age.

One day we all were sitting on the hill, across from the park during one of the parties; everyone was having a good time without really going into the park, you could hear the music for blocks. On that hill, you could see the cute boys that were walking to the neighborhood store. My mom could also see me from the front porch.

On this, I would learn how living in my house would affect me. The adults had alcohol in coolers, and they said we could have some as long as we stayed on the hill, and didn't leave their sight. Well, you know what happened to this lightweight, I was underage and drunk. *I was going straight to hell* I thought. I told them that I was going home, and they watched me make it there.

I walked through the door and no one was in the living room, so I hurried to my room, I laid down. BIG mistake; the next thing you knew, everything I had eaten and drank, was coming back up. I couldn't move, the room was spinning out of control. Then it happened, she came into the room and she lost it, "YOU HAVE BEEN DRINKING!" I said "No I have not!" and she yelled for my dad to come pick me up so she could clean me up.

I knew that I was going to be in deep, deep shit. My mother was still yelling and cussing, so she came back to my room." When you sober up, your ass is mine!" The fear of Jesus and Satan flew into me. The next morning, when I woke up, I felt like crap. My head was still spinning and there she was, standing over me asking me when I was going to get out of the bed. I told her that I couldn't. Then I threw up on her shoes. Needless to say, she walked away mad. An hour had gone by, then she returned. What was about to happen was shocking. My mother apologized for accusing me of drinking; she called the doctor's office and they told her that there was a virus going around and that was what was wrong with me. She stayed home that day and I got soup and ginger ale. I was never going to do this again, or was I?

Yes! 8th grade here I am. You would have thought what I went through during summer break would have stopped me. Oh no, before school, not every day, at least 3 days a week, I would sneak some of Mom's gin out of the bottle and put it in my drink to take to school (Trust me that is such a dumb thing to do.) On the ride to school, my friends and I would guzzle it down. By the time we got to school, we all had rubber band legs. At first, I felt bad, but then I remembered, I'd see my mom do this all the time. This went on for a while, where we all took turns bringing the juice until that one day I came home.

Yes, into drama. My mom was going in on my brother for drinking her alcohol. I ducked into my room; she told him that he had to replace it and "it bet not" happen again. From there, he came straight into my room and told me that he knew I did it.

To keep his mouth shut, I had to keep his room clean for at least a month. UGH. His room was a horrible place to go into until one day I was cleaning, and there it was, his shoe box. That shoe box I would hear him talk about on the phone.

There it was right there in front of me. Should I touch it, should I open it, what should I do? I did what any nosey kid would do. I opened it, "Oh My God!" It's a shoebox full of joints, Mary Jane. *Should I snag one or tell Daddy?*

The Friday night football game was in a few days, what harm would it do? I grabbed four, because that was how many of us were going to the game. When I got on the bus the next day, I told the girls what I had done; they were excited, but also just as nervous as I was.

Friday came and we were dressed, ready to walk to the game. We had a good mile or so to go. Not a big deal to kids; once we were clear of my house and my friend's house, we lit them up, walking like we were grown women with a Joint in our hands. I was choking, so were the others, then one said, "My mom and brother do this all the time and for it to work you have to choke." I said "ok", cough, cough, cough.

I was starting to feel really green. By the time we got to the game, I was seeing three of everything, trust me; when I say three, I mean three. The 1st quarter of the game was over and I was now just seeing two. What I was about to see two of, I wish I had gone the other way. It was my brother; he had his crew with him. They were walking towards me and my friends; he had a smile on his face until he got close.

I forgot that when you smoke, the smell stays with you. *UGH, I am toast.* "What's up sis?" then the smile disappeared. At this point, he was standing next to me. I saw the look of "oh crap", so I played it off, "Hey Man, what's up?" He leaned over, and said, "You have been in my shit, haven't you?" I was like, "Me? Nah, why would I do that and what shit are you talking about?" Then it happened; I couldn't keep a straight face for anything. Once I started, I couldn't stop, BUSTED!

My brother told me that he was moving it so I couldn't find it anymore, if he caught me with his stuff again, he was going to tell mom and dad and let them handle me. Yeah, I didn't want to deal with my mother at all and you would think seeing her, how she becomes when she has alcohol, I would stay away from it, but I didn't.

Still living the middle school dream, I was having a great year until the week before Christmas break. All the students were exchanging gifts, and I had gotten this cute little bear to give to one of my friends. We did our exchange and she said my bear that I gave her was dirty. It was not dirty; it was in the bottom of my back pack. She went the entire morning telling people she was going to beat me up for giving her a dirty teddy bear for a gift. I told everyone that the bear wasn't dirty, but oh no! I had to be big and bad. I said that I am not scared of her and if she wants to fight me, come on. *Please tell me why!* I went into the office and told the principal that this is what she was planning to do to me. When lunchtime came, I had gotten my food, sat down and could see her over to my right side. I could also hear, "I am going to get you." As soon as I finished my lunch and got up to take my tray back, she jumped me.

There was a circle of middle-schoolers yelling "fight, fight!" I had never done anything like this before in my life, but I was always told, "If someone puts a hand on you, then you need to protect yourself" so I did. Her first punch landed on my jaw, I thought that I was seeing stars. I automatically went into windmill mode; I know nothing about boxing, so I just started swinging and hoped I landed one punch.

The vice principal stepped in the middle and before I knew it, I had given him a swift kick in the personal area. I knew, at that point, I was going to be in deep, deep trouble, not only at home, but with him for his injury. We sat in the office together; the entire time she was talking about the dirty bear she got. She said when we got out of school that day, I was going to look as dirty as the bear.

We were called back to his office and the fear really kicked in. The vice principal now had a bag of ice on his leg, but we all know where he was placing that bag. "Ladies, what brings you into my office?" he begins. I was like *Hell, you were there, why are you asking that question? DUH!* So, my fight partner started yelling about me giving her a dirty bear as a gift, when she only spent $2.00 on my box of life savers. *OMG! Really you spent two whole dollars on me for something that will disappear in two days, I got you a lasting gift. This is crap!* When it was my turn, I explained that the bear was in the bottom of my backpack and it got smashed and moved around. The Vice principal stated that was a good reason and she should have believed me. Then came the big question, "What are we going to do about the punishment here?" Well, I already know when I walk into drama I am done, so there's not much you can do here that will stop that.

Our punishment was for the rest of the school year, we had to sit together for lunch. "Oh Geez, thanks for that." It took two weeks of us sitting together before we were able to talk to each other again. Friends never, but we can at least speak. Who would have thought that this wouldn't be the last time I would get into a fight? The punishment at "the drama that I live", like I said, would be far worse. In our back yard, there is this large beautiful Weeping Willow tree; I had to go get the standard three branches. My mother would braid them together, soak them in water and whip me. Drama I tell you, drama.

When my dad got home, He and my brother heard what had happened, along with my brother supporting my actions; with that being said, it turned into a full out brawl. I was used to the arguing, but I had never seen either of them place a hand on each other. I was trying to get to my dad, when my brother grabbed me. He said, "This is not the time to get in the middle." He had seen more of this action than I had, I was afraid and scared. My mother picked up my father and she threw him out the screened door. My father fell on the porch and rolled out onto the sidewalk.

By that point, I was screaming for her to leave my dad alone. At that point, she turned to me; you could see the hell in her eyes. At this point, I knew I was getting ready to have the taste knocked out of my mouth.

She raised her hand to me, just as it looked like it was getting ready to land on me, our next-door neighbor called out, "What are you doing? Let's go into the kitchen so you can calm down." As soon as she dropped her hand, I ran to the neighbor's house and stayed there.

Soon, there were police cars in front of my house; my little granny and Papa were there trying to take me back to their house. I told them that I could not leave my Daddy. I was standing outside with my grandparents and you could hear the argument as it continued inside the house. My dad walked out with an officer.

He didn't press charges? "What, why not?" I asked. "She's crazy!" My dad said, "Its ok, she is not well." *OH! Yeah, any fool can see that she's not, but why do we have to stay here and take this crap from her? UGH!* As I was leaving with my grandparents, my mother came bursting out of the door, "Where the hell do you think you are taking my daughter?" My Grandmother said, "Until you know how to act like a lady and a mother, she is going to stay with us." All hell flew back into her; as she went for the car that I was sitting in, my grandfather pulled off. All I could think about was leaving my dad behind. *What would happen to him and my brother if I wasn't there?*

I made it to my grandparents' house, then I told my Grandmother that I was worried about my dad. Less than 20 minutes later, my dad showed up at the house to check on me. I told him my fear of being there; he explained that my mother is an alcoholic, and along with drinking way too much, she is taking her medication, which doesn't go well together. To me, that didn't seem reasonable enough for me to believe, but it does explain some, but not all. I asked my dad if he was ok. He said just a little beaten up, but he was fine. The winter-time had come and gone; the flowers were blooming and I made it through the winter months without any drama. With warm weather, the drama would slowly return. Along with my mother, there was another neighbor on our street that was just as loud. He always had something to say about someone. If he wasn't talking trash about the neighbors, he would just walk up and down the street yelling strange things, almost like he was talking to another person but no one was ever there.

One Friday afternoon, all of the block was out, kids playing and having fun; then it happened, one of our neighbors walks down the street yelling that "He" was sleeping with my father. When my mother heard that, you can say he really poked the bear. Off the porch she came. For a large woman, she moved swiftly; they were in the middle of the street going at it. Here comes the police again. I am sitting on the sidewalk in tears. I said to myself, *I can't continue to stay here and or go on with this.* I had planned out how to run away; I could always get myself out of the door, but not much further than that.

It was getting to the point where the police knew the entire block by name, they were called so much. I wasn't sure whether to feel safe or just embarrassed. I could be downtown hanging out with my friends and you would see a police officer in uniform, who would speak to you using your full name. How do you explain to friends that don't know your background story that the police come to your house on the regular? *UGH my life, the drama!*

I had some friends talk me into joining the scouts for the summer. It was fun; it got me out of the house, away from some of the drama two or three times. We would go on trips and do things around the neighborhood, to earn our badges. The biggest thing every year was the cookie badge. My mother worked in one of the large hospitals in our town. She would take my cookie sheet to work that would put me at the top in sales or very close.

This summer, our counselors planned a camping trip that was going to be away from home and in the woods. I didn't want to go. I didn't want to be in the woods, no lights, no bathroom. How were we going to cook our food? I told Mom that I didn't want to go. She said that she didn't put all that work in to sell cookies for me to sit my ass at home.

Well, she soon found out that she too had to go with us; they got to stay in a cabin. While we were outside, each scout that was signed up, a parent had to be with them. I couldn't have laughed hard enough when she wasn't looking.

Oh, my goodness, I will never ever camp outside again. They took it to the extreme, getting your own firewood, fixing your own bean with your camping equipment and cold sandwiches. YUK! So, on our last night there, I had to go to the bathroom and there were no lights; it was dark, other than what was burning in the pit outside.

I was laying there wondering what I was going to do. They had us up off the ground like on a wooden deck with a tent. I came up with the bright idea, I just have to pee. What harm would it be just to go off the deck? I pushed the side of the tent out, and began to tinkle. Then I started to feel something was brushing my butt, I screamed and woke the entire campsite up.

We found out later that it was the tent flap that hit my butt. I knew I wasn't going to get in trouble because we all laughed; since we were up, we all sat around the fire laughing at me and telling ghost stories. It was great. I thought that when we got home that this would help me and my mom get to a better spot. She spent the entire ride complaining to my dad about how it went. I didn't say anything after that. My dad asked me how was it. I said I had fun; I told him about me waking up at the camp and how funny that was. He in turn and said, "I am glad you had fun." Mom looked at him, "What about me?' I had a horrible time." He said nothing. The rest of the ride was quiet.

I can say that this was an interesting summer. I will never, ever go camping again.

High School

ere I am, finally in the 9th grade ......

When I first got to high school, it was a very big building. There were a lot of students of different races that I had not been exposed to, which scared me. My friend from elementary school and I would eat our lunch in the bathroom just to not be seen eating and to stick together because we were both scared. As time went by, we both started making friends and eating lunch in one of the three cafeterias. Soon, we both would find our cliché. I was somewhat still hanging out with my nerdy friends with a mix of cheerleaders and athletes.

During the school year, things made a turn and one set of friends was trying to make me choose, to be with them or to not. You could tell that as the school year went by, some racial tension developed and the group was starting to divide. I had a good friend; he was one of those that didn't see color. He was dating a white girl so you know he didn't see color so I would usually hang out with them. I used to get teased that I was so light I could pass for white, so I could blend in easily. I never knew which one hurt more, the big forehead jokes, which by the way never stopped, or the color-passing jokes. I was told I was just sensitive and to let it go.

When you are in High School, you always want to fit in or be accepted, just like when you are in middle school. I wasn't into sports or clubs, so when the newest shoes came out, which was the Mia Clogs, all the girls were getting them. So, on one of our trips, I asked dad if I could get a pair of clogs; my dad was more than happy to get them. My mother was even in on the search. Little did I know I should have said I would like a pair of Mia Clogs. So we finally found a pair that I liked; I couldn't wait to get to school on Monday, to share my new shoes, to finally fit into a group.

I got to school, and it began, the picking on me so bad it took me back to when I was in middle school. The girls said that my shoes were fake, that I got them from a dollar store and they weren't even brown like the real ones. When I got home, I told my dad what happened at school today; my mom's reply was, "They didn't buy your shoes, so they need to be quiet until they do."

My dad saw the pain in my eyes. He knew I loved my shoes, but wanted nothing but to fit in. My dad got some dark brown shoe polish, took my shoes and started to change the shade of them. When he was done, they were a rich dark brown. Even if they weren't the Mia shoes, they were dark enough not to draw attention to them. I was so happy and grateful that he did that, while my mom on the other hand, said that he could have taken that energy, and fixed the kitchen cabinets.

I told my dad that I would help him paint them this weekend. This means that my mother would have to stay with one of the few friends that she had left. If she smells paint or cleaning supplies, she would get ill. There was a part of me that said, stay and sniff away. My church upbringing said not to do that. I had so much fun doing this project. My dad did the top cabinets and I did the bottom ones. While we waited for each set to dry, we cleaned down the walls, as well as the oven.

When Mom returned, did she say thank you to anyone for doing this? Nope. Her complaint was the color. I said "What color? The cabinets are white." Oops, shouldn't have done that. "Was I talking to your ass?" she said. Nope, but it came out and there was no putting it back. "Why are you upset? The kitchen is clean, new paint, all the dishes washed." She didn't like to wash dishes. "Why are you not happy?" She had no answer, she didn't speak to me or my dad until the next day; made for a great evening, nice and quiet.

We were starting to go to football games and what good times we had. It would seem like we had our freedom because there were no parents around, except those of players, cheerleaders and spectators. We had a great time. It had been a while since I had a drink or thought of sneaking one ever since my mom got on my brother and he covered for me. That was soon to come to an end; my friends had snuck in alcohol in the soda bottles and the party started.

Did I remember that you could smell alcohol from the last time I was almost busted? Nope. Did I care at the moment? I didn't think so, but I wasn't too worried, because my brother was picking me up when he got off from work, and he wouldn't say anything, because if he did, I would tell about the weed stash he has in the house and that would send my parents off.

We were having a great time. I couldn't tell you what the score was because we never went to the games to really watch, just to hang out. I noticed that the game was almost over and I was starting to wobble when I was walking; still no need to worry. My brother was coming, I am good to go. I got to the pickup spot, looked around and my brother wasn't there. I was getting really dizzy and then it happened. I looked to my left and there was my ride. Oh No! My parents were sitting there waiting to pick me up.

I could have died, because now I have to find a way to get my walk straight and not talk in the car. *Geez, how am I going to pull this off?*

I hopped in the car and the 1st thing out of my mom's mouth was, "Are you walking funny?" I pointed to my shoe and shook out a rock. *That will never happen again in life.* I said to myself, then they asked how the game was. I smiled and shrugged my shoulders. "Ok, so what's wrong with your mouth?" my mother asked.

I pointed to my jaw and made a grimace face and pulled candy out of my pocket and then I just laid down on the back seat. Oh, big mistake. The entire car started to spin; there was nothing I could do about it but lay there until dad got us all home.

However, dad didn't go straight home; he stopped at a fast-food restaurant to get dinner. *OH NO!!!!!!!* I wanted to yell "Please don't bring the smell of food in this car!" Too late, it was the smell of fries and then came the alcohol coming back up to decorate the floor of my daddy's car. Along with the smell of alcohol, my mother lost her shit. For a large woman, she managed to turn sideways in my dad's car. Once she could reach me, she knocked the shit out of me, she continued to wail on me until we got home. My dad opened his side of the door and when I got out, he said "Go lay down, we will talk about this later." Why did he say that?

You know that she has now flipped her wig, and is going in on him for what seems like he was taking my side. She began to throw the food at him while he was trying to clean out the car and my mess. I came outside through the back door to help him. I said how sorry I was for messing up his car. He said, "Pooh sit down." I could feel the tears starting to burn the rims of my eyes. "I want you to think about what you are doing. Look at what it is doing to your mother. I don't want you to turn out like this. You will not be able to get a job and support yourself; you will not be able to get the things you need or want in life because you are drinking." I felt so bad that I let him down; he was more worried than he was mad. Then the door swung open, he told me to go back in the house, walk by and say nothing, "Yes Sir."

I walked past her; she looked at me like she could really hurt me and she said, "Just like your daddy." She raised her hand like she was going to swing. I flinched, and ran into the house. What a long, long weekend this turned out to be. No one was talking to anyone. I couldn't go out for two months, which meant the entire basketball season. I wasn't allowed to stay after school for anything and I wasn't allowed to use the phone for the same amount of time.

This hell took me through football season right into Thanksgiving Break. As soon as it rolled around, I asked if I could go to my Little Granny's house just to get away from this crazy ass house. My request was granted. I got there on a Wednesday night and stayed until Sunday. On Thanksgiving Day, my Grandmother and I were up before the sun. We started with the turkey in the oven; I got to cut up the carrots, celery and onions for whatever she needed. We always shared a bottle of champagne. That was our thing that we did together and it was always fun to be in the kitchen with her.

My dad would stop by my little granny's cousin's house, Aunt

Pearl's, so she could join us for dinner. She was my little Grandmother's cousin and only living relative left. When my parents arrived, they were getting along. For once, we were all having a good time, until it was time for me to pass out the snacks and drinks and that is when my mom lost her cool. She flipped back to when I was drunk at the football game; why did she need to bring that up? My grandparents didn't have a clue that it took place; here, she is putting it out for the world. UGH! So, I had to hear from both grandparents about the dangers of drinking. Why did my Grandmother say, "Just look at your mother"? OMG! I wanted to say, "Everyone run!" To my surprise, my mother didn't say a word; nothing was said from her the rest of the evening. I would say rather nice, but that would be wrong. It was a great Thanksgiving until, it was time to go and you could hear my mother flipping out in the yard. All her anger and venom was pointing towards my father. All he did was drive them to the house.

My Grandmother went outside; she told my mother that if she has anything to say, she needs to speak to her and not her son.

That made it worse; my mom said you are always taking up for him, he does nothing wrong.

I was so glad that I wasn't going home with them, and I wished my dad would stay here with me.

When Sunday came, it was time for me to go home; that was one place I didn't want to go, but I knew when I woke up that I would be heading to school. I couldn't wait for summer to come so I could come back out to my granny to have a great time.

I was looking forward to the summer of doing nothing, eating good food and relaxing.

My dad did his best to make peace between everyone. On Saturdays, my dad and I would go out of town for day trips. We would head in one direction or another; most of the time they would be good trips and sometimes they would end with some tension, but this one trip really sticks out in my head.

My dad had to work a half day this particular Saturday; my Grandmother had fixed him some lunch to eat while my mom,

Grandmother and myself was heading into the store. I would have never thought a sandwich would cause such a big fight. As we were getting out of the car, my Grandmother reached over the seat and said to "Here's your lunch. You can eat this while you are waiting."

My mother turned to the side of the car, and let my poor little Grandmother have it. "Why couldn't you have packed lunch for everyone?" I replied, "My daddy said there are two in here, you can have one of them, it's not a problem." My mother smacked the sandwich out of my hand and replied, "If she didn't make one for me, what in the hell makes you think that I would want one of yours?"

While the back and forth went on, my Grandmother pulled me out of the car and we went into the store. She said to me, "Please get everything you want. This is granny's last trip. I can't deal with your mother anymore." We always stopped at this all-you-can-eat place after every trip; this time, my Grandmother asked to be taken home.

I didn't see anything wrong with this. I got to stay until Sunday evening. *Let's go back*. This too sparked another argument, because my granny always paid for the late lunch we would have. My mother's remarks were, "You will feed your son, but won't take care of the rest of us." My Grandmother remained silent the entire ride home, while my mom just kept sputtering stuff under her breathe. When we got home, I jumped out the car to see my grandfather. He was so much fun. I asked him to take me to the garden so we can shoot a groundhog.

He turned to me and said, they were fighting again huh?" My Grandmother came through the door and said, "I am not going with them anymore." Then came my dad, then my mom, who sat in her favorite chair on the screened in porch, refusing to talk to anyone that was around us. My dad said, "We are going back home now. Pooh I will come get you tomorrow evening. I couldn't wait to go to the garden to watch my grandfather scare away the groundhogs.

Then you heard my Grandmother yelling, "You two get up here

now. I need you to kill this thing on the back porch." I had to go through the front door; the next thing you heard was POP, POP. It was an opossum back there. My Grandmother was so funny, "Why didn't you scare it off the porch before you killed it?" I tried hard not to laugh, she said, "You are going to clean up this mess." Too funny.

Eventually, Sunday came, time to go home.

No child should ever fear going home, I was that child. I never knew what was going to happen or when it was going to. Would there come that day that she snaps and knock me out when my dad or my brother wasn't around? This is what goes through my mind when I have to be at home.

Tenth grade, *all I could say was that 'I am 3 years away from getting out of this house. I know I shouldn't be counting down when I am going to leave, but if you lived the hell that I do every day, you would count down too.'* It was the same thing at least three times a week; if you walked into the house and the music was playing loud in the kitchen, then a fight would have taken place or one was brewing. She would always be in the kitchen when she was mad, sitting at the table, staring off into space. You better not dare come in and not say something whether she was pissed or not; if you didn't say anything to her, that would make whatever hell she was about to rain down on us worse. On those days, you could hear my parents fighting in their room; it wasn't hard to hear, my room was next to theirs.

I was settling into high school like most kids. I wasn't the cheerleader, or a sports person; I was just the nerdy kid that had a few friends, but like the other girls, I wished I had a steady boyfriend. Well I thought wishes came true, that would soon be short lived. I met this guy a grade ahead of me; he would wait for me outside of my class. We would walk, talk and all was good. My parents would let me go to his house, which was two blocks from our house. The catch was, I had to stay on the porch outside. I could not go in the house.

Just like any teenager, we don't listen; my parents drove by twice to make sure I was sitting on the porch. We waved, then I said,

"Ok, they are not coming back again", so we went inside to watch TV. 30 minutes later, there was a knock on the door; in came my mother, who dragged me out the house, down the steps and into the car. I was told that I couldn't see him again.

Well, that's not going to happen; I would tell my parents I was hanging with my neighborhood buddies when I would be with him. I would have skipped school to stay with him, oh that was a mistake waiting to happen. I got caught skipping by a neighbor. She called the school to tell them she saw me walking around. Now, to return to school, I would need a parent to accompany me. Well hells bells. I wanted to live, but if I was going to tell them that, I might as well pick out my dress for burial. Little did I know that this wouldn't be the last time I would have to come home and face the music.

Well, I got back into school and I didn't have to tell my parents. You guessed it, my brother took me to school and because he was over the age of 18, he could speak for my parents. My brother told my guidance counselor that my parents were at work and couldn't take off to get me back into school. He requested that they write down everything that they needed to know and he would have them sign it and I would return it the next day. Whew! I get to live another day.

After that, I noticed that who I thought was my boyfriend was now acting a little strange; since I wouldn't skip school, or come to his house like I used to, I tried to talk to him. He told me that if I wanted to talk to him, come to the house this evening; it was said in a friendly, yet hateful tone. After school, I went to his house, only to find out that this was a test. He wanted to see just how far I would go with him, which was not far. Even if I wanted to have sex with him, all I could think about was what my mother would say.

The next day, he was no longer talking to me. I was crushed. So as the weeks went by and I was hanging out at the park with my friends; this girl walked up to me and said she was going to kick my ass for messing with her boyfriend.

"Ok..." I said, "Who is your boyfriend?" When she said his name, my heart dropped. She started teasing me. She said he left me because I wasn't giving it up. By this time, there was a crowd of people around waiting for something to go down. At that point nothing happened, she just walked away and told me to watch my back.

When I got home, I was in tears; my parents asked what was wrong and I told them what had happened. My dad was upset. He went into the kitchen, grabbed the broom and went outside. A few minutes later, he came back in with just the handle of the broom. He said, "Don't let anyone put that kind of fear into you. Take this broom handle, and go beat the shit out of her! Nobody pushes you around. Do you understand what I am saying? You have two choices, deal with her or you deal with us."

"Ok," I said, with fear now in my heart bigger than ever; do I walk down the block with my crew looking for her or what? Well, off I went with a broom handle in hand, my group of friends walking with me. I stood outside her house yelling for her to come out; a lot of nasty words were exchanged, then she said "If you are going to fight me like you say then put down that stick and let's go!" My thoughts are, *so what in the hell am I to do?*

We, meaning the group and myself walked back to my house. I threw the handle in the yard and headed back to her house. She and her gang were heading my way; we all met one block from my house and the throw-down began. There was no one there to stop the fight; we battled hard in the middle of the street. I was scratched up and bloody. It didn't stop there; we ended up in the park at the same time and the fight picked up where it left off. The park was full of people, so they were able to stop the fight, but not before a lot of us were bloody, and scratched up.

That Monday, I got on the bus. Mr. Man tried to talk to me, to tell me how sorry he was. He had never had two girls fight over him. He also told me that if she wasn't pregnant, we would still be together. "Lies," I said. "You didn't want to be with me anyway because I didn't put out, so you go ahead and stay with her." I then said, "Wait! I was fighting a pregnant girl?" His response, "I didn't think it would come to this." I told him that he was a low life for putting us both in this shit!

When I got to school, I was teased saying I got my butt whipped; others that supported me told me that I did the right thing and she would have kept coming after me until it happened. I said that boys are not worth this aggravation. Fast-forward, Prom is here. I wanted to go, but my parents wouldn't let me, because they said that proms are where everyone has sex after prom was over; I was going to have no parts of that. Crushed, but ok with it. What made things worse... not that I wasn't able to go, I had told this guy I would go with him. After my parents told me I couldn't go, I had to tell him that my parents said no. He was not happy. He never let me live it down, but we always stayed friends. There's always next year, right?

End of another good school year, grades were average but passing, which mean I wouldn't hear any flack out of her. I asked if I could go to summer school (just so I wouldn't be in the house with her) and my dad said, "If she wants to go, let her go." So that made summer fun for me. I got to get a class out of the way for next year and I was away from the drama at home.

During the summer, I would keep the house clean just to keep the arguments down. Some days, I would even cook dinner, until one day, my dad told me how much he liked my spaghetti dinner. My mom lost it; she was like, "Is there something wrong with the way I cook it?" Dinner went downhill from there. It didn't stop me from cooking; it just stopped him from saying anything in front of her.

Now that I am in high school, my trips to my grandparents during the summer all but stopped. I would see them every Sunday. I started to spend more time becoming a small version of my mother. I would hang out in the park during the week and sneak drinks on the weekend. Get into arguments with friends at school. Not know when I was going to snap if something was said wrong.

I guess you can say I am a late bloomer. I was feeling bad; my stomach was in pain like I had never felt before. We were at the park and one of my friends said there was a spot on my shorts.

When I got home, there was blood everywhere. This is the time when a girl would need her mother. I was scared to say anything to her, not knowing that this was natural. I should have remembered from elementary school; we spent most of our time giggling.

I called my friend, what do I do? She said she had all of the stuff I needed to help me through it. I was so sick. My mom came into my room, and the first thing she asked was if I was drinking. I told her that I hadn't been drinking and I didn't feel good. She left my room, told my father to come in the room to make sure I was telling the truth. REALLY!? The nerve of this woman. I am on the floor of my room in a knot. Of course, I am sick. What am I supposed to tell my father? Hey dad I started my period. Like that was really going to happen. My dad leaned over, he asked if I was ok? Did I want to go to the doctor? I told him that it was something that I need to talk to a lady about. He called my little Grandmother and one of my friends to come help me. The help he got for me was not received very well. My mother asked why didn't I tell her that this was going on. His response, she tried to tell you but you accused her of drinking. That started the one thing I can't stand, yes, a fight. You have. Always taken up for her, she can never do any wrong. This is a summer that I wouldn't forget.

Junior year, I was excited because there was only one year left before I was out. I was put in one of the hardest teacher's History classes. I was going to stick it out because they said if you got a C in her class that was like an A. After my second test with the 27 on it, I had to leave that class. Then, I was put in what was the easiest history class; I walked in and there was every athletic guy in the school.

This was going to be a struggle. Here is the ugly duckling student, in there with these guys. As I looked around, I saw a few people in the class that I knew, which made it easier to be in there. Did it stop the picking on me? I would say not. When I had to go in front of the class, they (the athletes) would pick on me about my hair and what I was wearing. It was a class I didn't want to go into, but I had an A in the class, so I would stick it out.

They changed my classes around this time, I ended up in a class with the fool I was claimed to be fighting over. This, by far, was more uncomfortable than the history class I was in. He had the nerve to pick his seat next to me, why? What in the hell could he gain from sitting next to me other than making me upset?

Once he realized that I could care less for him, he relocated his seat. Then the year started to get better. There were actually a few guys that wanted to go out with me, who didn't see me as a nerd pushing to get my grades. I knew that the next year, I should be applying to college. The time had come when we were all getting ready for prom again. How shocked was I, when my parents said I could go, but with a curfew, *ok I will take it!* I thought that I would get a chance to go with the guy I didn't get a chance to go with. He wouldn't take a chance on me, so I went with the first guy that asked me. I told him I had a curfew and he said that was ok; he just wanted to hang out with me, and have fun.

I was looking forward to going dress shopping. UM no that

wasn't happening... my mom had someone make my dress. *WHAT in the frosty hell, here we go again looking like a bag of rocks going out.* I couldn't say anything because I didn't have any money.

When it was finished, it did look kinda cute. I rocked it. When I got to the prom, I had people who thought the dress was cute; I relaxed and had a good time until it was over or time for us to leave. My date took me back to his house so he could change. "Um, why couldn't you just drop me off?" I said. "You still have time before you need to go home, let's chill and watch TV," he replied. Not feeling really comfortable about this, I did. All I could remember was my parents saying what happens after prom.

I couldn't believe that all we did was watch TV. With 30 minutes to go, he took me back home and there he gave me a peck on the cheek. "Ok who is the guy? I thought he was in the group of guys that just wanted one thing. Am I getting into my own head? I don't want to let my guard down and something happens. Well, we became really good friends and hung out on the weekends.

together, you never saw me without him. I thought, *"Hey could he be the one?"* We will soon find out.

We both agreed that we couldn't see each other for more than hanging out buddies. He didn't want to end his senior year with a relationship. He said, "You know that when you go off to college, 90% of the time, a high school relationship never lasts." I thought he was crazy, but I didn't push the issue. I was ready for summer; that would put me one year away from my all-time dream of leaving this house.

Summer was finally here; I swear it was like I had rolled back in time. I was hanging out with some school friends who were seeing guys that lived 20 miles away, so when they asked me to hang out with them, that's when all the trouble began. One guy in the group, Tre' was hanging out around me; we seemed to be the only two without someone. So, it seemed that this was planned this way. He was really nice. We started to see each other and he would come to my house and pick me up and we just had a really good time. This was until a girl named Rosie came up to the both of us, and went off. She said, "I knew you were seeing him, why are you with him?" She slapped the crap out of him, I said to myself, *"Lawd here we go again."* I said I wasn't going to fight another soul over a guy; this time, I am staying true. I told Rosie that if this is what is going on, then I have no issues leaving him alone. She replied, "Yes, he is my man." That's when Tre' spoke up; I am not with you, I took you out but this is not going to work with us. I am with her now and that's the way it's going to be.

These interactions went on for weeks. I would get calls from her and she would give me death stares when she saw me in the street. Sometimes she just walked up to me like she was going to hit me, but didn't. I knew that when school started again, I would see her in the hallways. I hoped by the time we were back in school that she would be over it. Only time would tell.

It was finally here, the year that I have been waiting for, my Senior year. This meant that once I graduated, I would be free from the drama I live in. My Senior year was awesome or so I thought. I had a boyfriend; my grades were rocking and I had my driver's license; this girl was loving life. We are supposed to enjoy our senior year in high school, and take in all that it has to bring. However, just a few months prior to graduation, that was not the case. We had a school newspaper, which was a pretty good little paper for the high school. Updated information, game times and fun tidbits. It was worth the quarter that we paid for it.

This week was a paper unlike any we had seen before. The gossip of the article in the paper spread throughout the school like wildfire. What was it you say? It was the most racial-written paper I had ever seen. I was raised to not see race because of the friends I had. Today, I see red, I see black!

It referred to our "Black" students, as the N-word... that we were only there to get heat and free food. It went on and on. I think by the time it got to the majority of the school, there was no putting out this fire. All of the Black students left the classrooms, the hallways were not a safe place for anyone to be, trash cans were being turned over or thrown and teachers began to lock the doors for protection. All of the students that were a part of this began to go outside. By this time, our local news channel was there, recording everything. The next thing I knew, I was being pushed up on the school bus. We were all packed in there like fish in a store fish bowl.

The next thing I remember is, the bus starting to rock, as fast as it started to rock, it stopped. The door opened and on stepped our Black Vice principal. "If you want to graduate, you have 30 minutes to get off this bus!" Ok now that scared me; I was saying to myself, *if I ever want to get out of my house, go to college, I need to get off this bus!*

Some started to leave the bus, saying they needed to graduate; I too started making my way off the bus, oh but we were greeted with a sheet of paper when we stepped off. The person handing the papers said, "Go to your right." I looked at the paper and it said I was suspended for ten days. What the Hell? I got off the damn bus, why am I getting suspended?

I said to him, "If you are going to suspend me, then I might as well stay on the bus." His response was if I didn't watch my mouth, he would add days to it. As a few more kids came off the bus, the thirty minutes were up.

Those of us that got off the school bus, had to sit on the sidewalk until our parents came and the others on the bus couldn't get off until they got all of the names. Did I hear him correctly? I have to wait here for Who? Awe hell nah! I tried my best to tell them my parents were at work and called my brother. Too damn late, the car was pulling in. We couldn't get our books or anything from the school.

I wanted to find a hole, and dive in it at this point. I was walking over to the car; it was like a slow mile to my death. I knew that this was going to be the end of me. I would not get married, have kids or enjoy leaving my house.

When I got to the car, I greeted them like nothing was wrong. I said, "so how is everyone? I guess you heard I get to stay home for ten days huh?" My mother was very calm; in a low breath, she said, "Get your ass in the car." She waved out the window to the

Vice Principal, and yelled, "We will handle this." Oh shit, my life

is really flashing before my eyes. What in the frosty hell is about

to happen?

It was a silent ride home; no one said anything to anyone. We

pulled up in front of the house and Dad said, "We are going to sit

out here for a few minutes." Mom took her seat in her favorite

porch chair; Dad and I were on the stoop. They were both staring

at me, and then Dad said, "We have decided to let your ten days

be your punishment, because you were standing up for what you

thought was right... but while you are out of school, you will not

be hanging out and doing nothing."

I got a list of things to do around the house. I couldn't watch TV

during school hours or go outside to the park. The ten days went

by fast. I was back in school busting my chops to get all my work

caught up and take a test that I had missed while I was gone.

I had applied to several schools, but the one I really wanted to go

to was in North Carolina. I got accepted to both schools. One in

Virginia and the other was my dream school in North Carolina.

My dad was happy for me, but he asked me to make sure that if I really would like to go to the school, if so, could I go to one in VA, so that if anything happened, he would be able to come to the school on short notice.

All that he has done for me, that was the least that I could do for him. I accepted the offer to the Virginia school. Now, I have to focus on graduating in a few weeks. I had caught up on all the work from the situation. I just had this English paper that I needed to knock out the park. I knew if I stayed at home, I wouldn't be able to get it done the way I wanted to. I asked my dad if he could take me to Little Granny's, so that I could complete my last project so that I could graduate? He agreed. My dad dropped me off on Friday and when I got there, my Grandmother had dinner ready.

She told my dad to stay, but he said no, because it would just start a fight. My granny, being the sweet one that she is, boxed up dinner for both of them for my dad to take home. Who knew this would start something that my Grandmother couldn't stop?

Saturday, I had papers all over the floor in my room; I wrote and rewrote the paper until my fingers started to hurt. By Sunday, I was done. I think out of everything I did in all 4 years of school; this was the one that I was most proud of. It was time for our Sunday dinners at my Grandmother's; we managed to enjoy our dinner without any issues, until it was time to go. My mother went into the kitchen with the box my Grandmother had sent home. She started to fill up the containers, to take the leftovers home. At first, my Grandmother was going to stop her, then she realized if she just let her get the food, it would make things easier for my dad. So, from this point on, my Grandmother would send food home every Sunday without fail. On the days when we didn't eat or stay, we would pack up the food, and take it back home.

On Monday, I walked into English class on cloud 9. When I turned in my paper, the teacher looked up and said, "This is nothing like what you would turn in when I had you in the 9th grade." My class work I did in her class was not my best. She told the class that she would have them ready for us on Friday. The week couldn't go by fast enough for me. Friday finally came, and she was giving out our papers, I couldn't wait to get mine. Something was really wrong; everyone got theirs but me.

I raised my hand and she looked at me, and said just a moment. I said to myself, *Dam! I failed this one, now how bad will my grade be? Will I be able to graduate?* She started talking, letting the class know that she was very proud of us all and the effort that we put in. She had one paper that got 250 out of 250. She reached towards her desk. It was my paper, I thought I was going to cry. The only issue with my paper was punctuation. I couldn't wait to get home.

Mom and Dad were waiting for me. My teacher had called my house to let them know about my paper, they were taking me out to eat. I guess they too were proud of what I had done. I was so excited; we went through an entire meal with no issues. While we were out, my mom said we should get my stuff for graduation.

Yes, I was going shopping. I got the cutest dress and shoes. In my mind, *I was so ready for this day to come and was hoping it went without any issues*. We had a few shots of liquor before graduation, and prom. Plans were being made for parties. I couldn't pick which one I was going to. I remembered that whichever one I did go to, I would have to take my boyfriend. I kept forgetting that I had one of those. Don't know how with all the drama I went through in the summer-time.

The time had come to go to the prom; you would not believe what I did? Yes, I wore the same dress that I wore last year. What was really funny, no one recognized it. Then I thought to myself, *why does everyone put so much effort into getting a dress that they are only going to wear once*? We had such a good time at the prom, all of my friends were there. We took our senior prom seriously because we all knew this was the last time that we would gather like this.

After it was over, I went home to change my clothes to go back out. Yes, back out; my parents really liked the new guy and didn't have a problem with him. I should have paid attention to that, but didn't; we got some fast food and went to a park and chilled.

Then it hit me, *this fool is going to try to do the after-prom thing,* "Oh Crap" and I am out in the middle of nowhere, (or so I thought).

I was sitting on the hood of his car and he had positioned himself right between my legs. He said, "I have to tell you something." In my mind, the only thing I could think of was, *"oh shit" what is he going to do to me?* This fool says "I love you", what? I tried not to laugh, but this right here was not what I was after. My response, "WOW thanks", then he went on to say that he would never leave me or hurt me. Ok, this turned out to be way too much for a prom night, but at least I made it back home the way I came there.

That time had finally come, the time that I had been waiting for since kindergarten, yes graduation. The day that I would be out of that house, and be free from hell. Graduation was here, I was more than excited. Nothing could kill this feeling, or could it? I couldn't believe how long it took for this ceremony to end. It seemed like 8 hours, but it was really only three. My last name was in the middle, so it took forever to get to me, as well as to end.

There were a lot of people in the parking lot after graduation. It took me a little time to locate my family.

I have told you what type of person my mother is, throughout the high school years, or better yet, my entire life. No matter what is going on, she needs the spotlight; today was no different. After graduation, we were taking photos; everyone from friends to family was there. I took a photo with my dad before I took one with her and all hell broke loose.

I noticed that my mother was starting to look funny, like something pissed her off. I am not stupid; I am not going over there to find out. As we were standing around, she was very quiet. As we approached the car, she turned out of natural reflex. I duck, with my hands now in front of my face.

Then she started this rant in front of my friends, classmates, who I purposely kept away from her. She went into a rant that the fire station couldn't put out, all because my dad took the photo before her; then the other bomb dropped. "It would have been nice of you to take a picture with me," she declared. Oh Shit! Is this what she is really upset about? I said "Mom, that's not a problem, when we get home, we can take one." Her response was, "If you didn't think enough of me to take one when we were there, then don't entertain me with one now." She turned back around and didn't say anything else to me for the rest of the evening.

On the other hand, she did throw it in my father's face that I took the time out to take photos with him and didn't take one with her. *Why are we pulling my dad into your personal issues?* For the record, my daddy hates taking photos and I pulled him in. I wanted to remember all that he gave up for me, how much I really appreciated it. Little did I know this was not the only special day she was yet to take the spotlight for.

The one thing that I didn't understand with this was that my mother could go from negative zero to five hundred in a heartbeat, and she could return just a fast.

When she comes back, her ability to make you feel like shit, even when you didn't do anything, was crazy.

Soon, we all returned to my house; I couldn't figure out why, my boyfriend was walking was walking slowly behind me. I knew he had just gotten off from work maybe he was tired.

When we got into the house, I turned around to see why he was walking slow. He had my graduation gift; he handed me a large bag and said congratulations. When I opened it, there she was, a black cabbage patch doll. I am not sure how in the world he got it, because during that time, when they were super popular, people were in stores fighting over them and here I was with one. Her name was Petra; it was the best gift I ever got. I was so excited; others thought I was crazy. I took it out of the box and jumped in my mom's lap; everyone started taking photos and she finally started talking again. I knew if I didn't do something, she would take it out on daddy while I was out for the night. I couldn't have that. After the photos, I had family and friends waiting for me; we were heading out to have fun.

Some family members would say to me. "You need to break up with him now, because when you get to college, there are going to be so many guys to choose from that you don't want to have something at home and can't enjoy yourself." I was like, "Come on guys, that can't be true; we have been together a year, I can't just dump him on a whim like that. It seems so cold and so mean." For some reason, it stayed in the back of my mind.

During the summer, I took a job at a big box store; I wanted some money to take with me to school. While working there, I met some great people to work with. There was one person that I got along with well, her name was Elise. If I wasn't hanging out with my boyfriend, I was with her. She liked to do things that I like to do, go places I like to go, we just clicked as friends. When I hung out with her, drinking was not an issue. I never really thought about drinking when hanging out with Elise. There was no stress, no drama. It was two crazy girls having the best summer ever.

We would go to the local university; we would just go up there and hang out. Then the next thing, we started getting invited to the parties that the summer school students were having at the university. I made sure to invite my longtime friend growing up. It. Was great to have them join me and Elise e for fun.

Between working, hanging out with friends and going out with my boyfriend, there was little time to be at home. What a blessing or was it? One day, I was off from work with no plans with anyone, then I noticed that the house was looking kinda' rough. Remember, my mother doesn't clean and/or lift a finger, but she could shop like hell. Her big thing was to shop from a company that sold items through a catalog, and delivered them the house by a rep. Our house looked like a damn department store.

Therefore, I started to clean up, pick up things and put them where they should be. She came home from work and lost it. "I wish you wouldn't touch my things when you and your father clean up, I can never find anything." I did it again, I opened my mouth before I thought about what I was about to say. "The way things are thrown all over the place, how can you find anything like this?" Oh Shit, I said it out loud, and right next to her. First swing I missed; the second one landed right in the middle of my back. "You need to remember who you are talking to like that." She went into the bathroom and I continued to clean up and not let her see that she got to me. When dad got home, he said how nice the house looked; that set her off. We were now getting to the point where, this shows she puts on, we had outgrown it.

I had also cooked dinner. While in my room, I would start packing the stuff I wanted to take with me, so when that day came, I wouldn't have to waste one second getting out. During my senior year, I had gotten my driver's license. I was pulling around in everyone's car, and couldn't wait until the day I could have my own. I was taught how to drive by my brother's girlfriend, Jamie. She was really cool to learn from. There were also days she would let me drive her to school. I really liked her and she always made sure that when they went to the amusement parks, my brother would bring me with them.

So now, my boyfriend was insisting that I learn how to drive an automatic. Definitely a sight to behold; we were in a middle school parking lot; I just knew that I was stripping his gears. The car would jerk so hard, when I didn't do it correctly, we both almost hit our heads on the dashboard. Within a few weeks, I got it down; he would let me drive from my house to his. This trip was about 20 minutes one way.

Summer was coming to an end and it was time for me to head off to college. I was excited, yet scared. This was what I had been waiting for since kindergarten. So why do I feel so sad? Is it because I am leaving my family, as crazy as hell as they are? Am I worried about being on my own? I am not sure what to think of these bittersweet feelings.

College

The day I had waited for was finally here, we were packed and ready to go to my school in Virginia, only one hour and forty-five minutes away from my house, with the way my daddy drove. I was nervous yet excited, so off we went – all four of us... Dad, Mom, the boyfriend and myself.

I was overwhelmed at the size of the school, but was ready to take it on. My dorm had 6 floors. Depending on who you asked, I was lucky to be on the top floor. At the very end, the view from the top was amazing. You could almost see the entire school. The time had come to say goodbye; I was not sure why my mom was having all of these extra tears, was it because I wasn't there anymore to clean and cook? I know that sounds mean, but that is my heart. As the boyfriend and my dad walked away with her, I completely lost it.

This was not what I was supposed to be doing at this time. Was I supposed to be dancing all the way down the hall to the rickety old elevator? My heart strings were being pulled as we separated. My dad turned to me, "Take care Pooh... if you need anything, let your mom know and we will get it to you." Tears steadily rolled down my face. As my boyfriend and my dad walked away with her, I completely lost it. Then it was the boyfriend's turn; I got a big hug and a kiss even bigger, who knew this would be the last time.

Shortly thereafter, I went back to my room; my roommate was there with a few other girls who were out in the hallway. They said, "Hey, we are hungry, want to walk with all of us to the food place around the corner?" "Sure," I said. While walking to get food, we were all introducing ourselves. Little did we know that we would be the group that stayed together for the 4 years to come.

As we walked to the food place, we all were talking about the boyfriends left behind; one of them said, "Hey I dumped mine before I got here." Well damn, I was thinking *why would you do that?* I would soon find out. We all got to the restaurant... and there they were. It was like an all you could eat buffet, of guys. Different build, height, color... everything. I was there five minutes; over walked Curtis. Who knew that he would be the reason for the letter I would write in three days?

It was like a magnet of some sort. Curtis and I, we just clicked. We started talking as he walked back with me to my dorm. He gave me his number and asked me to call once I knew our floor phone number. In my mind, I was saying "Day damn one, Day damn one". My roommate was teasing me, saying, "That didn't take long." We both just laughed, then she said, "When are you going to write that letter?" I just dropped my head and laughed; *I have a boyfriend at home... this is crazy!*

For more than one reason, I am glad my dad talked me into or let's say, asked me to go to the school in Virginia. I will say my dad was consistent in sending money to me. Every Thursday, I would get an envelope from home. I hope you all are ready for this. Enclosed was $7.00, yes seven. I asked my dad what's up with the $7.00. Could I get $10.00? His response was, "It's a dollar a day, you have room and board, and a lunch plan. There's really not a need for you to have that much money down there." *Whatt!!?*

I told my Little Grandmother about what seemed to be a horrible situation. She went to her bank and set up a checking account for me; this way, she would be able to put money in as needed. What a help that was. I was not allowed to tell my father. Oh, we had a little secret between us, it was something we would laugh about when I came home.

The first three weeks of school, you could not separate Curtis and myself. Well let me share week two of us being together, yes, I wrote the letter and mailed it back home, to the boyfriend. I felt bad; I couldn't see myself at school spending all this time with Curtis, and seeing him. That was not right and, in my heart, I knew it was wrong.

Our Labor Day weekend was finally here. My parents picked me up and I could not wait to get home to my Grandmother's cooking. All the way home, my mom quizzed, "Why did you dump that boy? He has been at the house every afternoon asking what he could do to make this up to you."

UGH! Really? Is this what I am going to have to deal with for four days? When we got home, it was nice to see my room with its pink, floral wallpaper. Oh, how I missed my bed.

It wasn't long before there was a knock on the door. My mom answered it and yelled for me. Of course, I was like *"What part don't tell him I am here did she miss?"* I might as well just pull the Band-Aid off and talk to him. *Oh Lord, this fool is sitting here crying...* "What's up?" I said. His response was, "What the hell do you mean what's up?" I was like, "You are here when I clearly told you we are done". He said, "I need to hear it from your mouth, and tell me how this happened so fast." "I know you really don't want to know that now, do you?" I replied.

Ok "It's over, I don't want to see you anymore, I am seeing someone else. Are you happy now?"

Well damn, here comes the tears again. "I am sorry I hurt you, but I couldn't spend time with this person knowing that I was seeing you. That would not be correct or fair to you. I know this is crazy, I will give being friends a chance; I don't need you to take it the wrong way." From there, he left the house and I didn't see him anymore during my four-day visit.

Now my happiness at home turned into, 'how to make me feel bad!' I got to hang out with my friends and family. I also got to eat some really good food. During this time, there was not one outburst from my mom. I knew she was heading in the right direction now. It was nice to see this side of her. Maybe she was coming around, learning to enjoy life and not make everyone else miserable.

Well, that was short-lived. On our way back to school, we stopped at my little Grandmother's house. My Grandmother had fixed this large box of my favorites to take back. This Sunday, she didn't fix my parents a box, and that's when the shit show began. My mother wanted to know where their box was. She explained that she spent her time working on food for me this week...- that she thought my mom could cook one Sunday. "Oh no! Run granny," I said. Of course, my dad stepped in before the shit hit the fan. He told my mother that they were going to stop somewhere to eat on the way back home. However, she still continued to cut her eyes at my Grandmother. From the dining room, my grandfather called my mother into the living room to talk to him. Whew! Thanks Papa, you saved the day again. So, our conversation continued with laughter, just a good time. Now I have to leave, to return to school. Part of me is missing them, the other part can't wait to get back to school, to see Curtis.

Back on campus, the first semester I busted my butt. Even though I was with Curtis, I managed to get on the Dean's list. This was a big deal for me. I was proud of myself, along with my family. You see, I was the only one to go to school; this was thrown in my face often. *You need to stay focused, so on and so on.*

Now I was starting to get used to campus life and the party scene. The party scene was just a little too much. At this point, I started to have big brothers looking out for me; it just so happens they would all be in different fraternities. That means, I had access to all the parties as the little sister, but here's where the twist of my past comes in. At every party I went to, there was drinking, sometimes drugs, all depending on who was throwing the party. The more I partied, the more distance that came between Curtis and myself.

The demons of my past came rushing back. I could drink with the best of them; I didn't have any concern of what could happen to me. *I was protected by my big brothers... right?* The partying continued; I have no idea how I still maintained being on the Dean's list for another semester. I didn't lose that, but I lost Curtis. He said that I was no longer the person he knew, or wanted to hang out with. I was wondering just what did that mean, and why would he say that. I was crushed. I thought, *is this what my old boyfriend felt like when I dumped him? Man, this hurt.*

Now I was somewhat alone when the weekend came. I was ready to party; my friends knew that if they stayed with me, I could get them into most parties for free. Weekends were our favorite, until I noticed that my grades were starting to slip. I had to ease up on the partying, to focus on my grades. One of my "brothers" worked as a residence assistant; the problem was, he was in the same dorm as Curtis. That didn't stop me. I needed help getting my grades up. He was a tutor for the school, so I was able to go to him to get help. Now, I only had three weeks before school was out to get these grades up. I was starting to feel stressed; the only thing that came to mind was drinking. I really thought that if I tried to drink and get my school work done, this would help. It didn't; the first test I got back; I think I might have passed out. The grade was so low, we are not going to talk about it.

At this point, what I do know, is that I was scared straight. For the last few weeks, I worked with this guy named Terrence, who was like my brother away from home, trying to get my grades up. I stopped or paused the partying on the weekends at his suggestion, to apply myself to getting my ass out of this problem. It worked; I didn't make the Dean's List this time, BUT! I was not on academic probation, and there would not be a letter to go home.

End of the school year came around and we all said our goodbyes. It felt strange that Curtis was nowhere to be seen; he was really pissed at me. I went home and got a job, for money to spend on stuff I wanted without hearing the lecture about how that is really not needed. I was also back to cleaning the house and cooking to keep the arguments down. I really didn't miss that at all; you would think that with me being out of the house that would help ease the arguments. Oh no, just the opposite; now we have new signs to let us know to be aware of drama.

My dad would say "Pooh, if she is swollen like a tick, don't mess with her." That means if she was sitting quietly, arms folded and not talking, she was upset. There was another sign we were used to; she would have that music blasting in the kitchen, to the point you couldn't even hear yourself or the TV. Man, this is nuts. When I would come home and the music was like that, I would turn my ass around and head right back out the door, to go sit on the guard rail at the end of our street and watch cars. Sounds boring, I know, but it was a safe place to be.

Three weeks into the summer, I got a call. I was shocked but somewhat happy, it was Curtis. "Hello, how are you doing?" I chirped. His response was that he was wrong, and he shouldn't have thought just because I was at the parties that I was being that girl. I asked, "What made you come to that conclusion?" and "What took you so long?" The reply I got was not one I took well; he said he had to talk to other people that were at the parties to see what I was doing, instead of believing me. I told him I had to go and would talk to him later.

Curtis and I kept in touch on and off throughout the summer. My mother on the other hand, there were days during the summer that I had fun with her. We would go shopping, laugh and have a good time; it's just when things didn't go her way, she would shut down and stop talking to me.

Once home, Dad was like, "Where are your grades?" I told him I didn't know, but here is what I know I got. This summer was different from all the other summers. My neighborhood friends and I started to spend time at the local college at their parties. Something about the party scene just attracted me. I couldn't stay away from a party. That is where I met another Frat brother that knew some of my friends. I said *this is going to be fun*. I worked and never missed a party.

This is a 360 from the girl who never went anywhere during middle school and high school; my brother would show up at the parties and make sure I stayed there. If I did anything wrong, he would tell mom and we all know what would happen. I remember that we all had to be in the house or on the street, when the street light came on. Well one night, that didn't happen. I was in the park with a guy just sitting there talking. I heard her yell my name; I thought if I didn't reply, all would be good. Some fool in the park said, "She's over here!" Why in the name of whip your ass would you say anything? I looked across the street and there she stood, looking like a pissed off bear, in a pink housecoat or robe and those pink sponge curlers. "If there is a God in heaven, take me now!"

This is an exaggeration, but I swear I felt the earth shake as she walked over, I could hear her cussing and the next thing I knew, my shirt was choking me and I was on my ass looking up at the sky. Please note, the sky was moving. Yes, she was dragging me through the park. How embarrassing was that? People laughing and pleading with her to let me go. When we got home, she beat the life out of me. I think she already knew what she was going to do, because she had the belt ready. At least I no longer had to get the switches off the Weeping Willow tree; she used to braid them and soak them in water and then whip me.

I was starting my sophomore year and was so glad when it was time to go back to school. I was looking forward to it because I got to pick my dorm and my roommate this year. Our dorm was right in the middle of everything. I didn't have to walk far to anything, this was great, or so I thought.

As the school year went on, my roommate and I became really good friends. We would eat together, go out and have fun. One day, I came back to the room and her boyfriend was there. I turned around and left. After he left, we had a talk about not having the opposite sex in the room unless we had talked about it before hand; she agreed.

About a month later, one night I was asleep. It was around midnight when I heard the door open; I thought it was my roommate going to the restroom. I went back to sleep, only to be awakened to the moaning sounds; he was telling her to be quiet. I was in shock; I couldn't believe they were doing this next to me. I got up and left the room, with my blanket in hand. I slept in the common area (this was a large living room where people hung out). An hour or so later, she comes out and tells me it's ok to come back to the room.

I said, "I am good right here, thank you." As soon as the sun came up, I was on the phone with my dad asking him if he could afford to have me move into a private room. I told him what happened and he was furious. He also called the head of housing and talked to them. Due to what happened to me, I could move across the hall to the empty room ASAP, and they wouldn't charge me for a single room because no one else was coming into the building.

I realized that having a roommate could have been the best thing for me. Having a room to myself, I soon fell back into the way things were at home growing up. I went back to the party scene, because Curtis and I were that 'on again-off again' couple. I said *these were supposed to be the best years of my life, so let's have them. I am one year away from being able to buy my own alcohol; once this happens, life is going to be great.* I always wondered why was I so excited about being legal to buy alcohol.

My partying started back up, and with a vengeance; there wasn't one I didn't miss. My big day had arrived, it was my birthday, and I had saved my money to make sure I got what I wanted. That evening, we walked over to the convenience store and I got a six pack of wine coolers. I was so happy; I had my friends take photos of me buying my first thing of alcohol.

What would be the chances that my birthday would be on a weekend? I cracked open one of the bottles and started drinking. Then one of the girls yelled that the Frats are having a house party. I yelled "Hell yeah, let's go, it's my freaking birthday!" We all piled in the car and off to the party we went. I only wished I knew what was about to happen. I was still chugging down my drinks when we arrived at the party; my legs were rubber, but that didn't stop me. When we got inside, there was an open bar. I continued to party, drink and dance, then things changed. One of the nicest looking Frat brothers came over to me, said he had been watching me for the last year, but never had the nerve to say anything. We know that crap you Frat brothers talk; I have seen many step shows, I am not crazy.

Then he started to make his moves; he said, "Why don't we go somewhere a little less noisy?" This is a house party, the only place we could go would be a bedroom. But ok, it's my birthday. Let's go talk. I was still throwing back the drinks like a pro. So, we got into the bedroom and we started talking, before everything went black. I woke up in the lobby of my dorm the next morning. I was very frightened; I didn't know what had happened to me. How did I get home, did he have sex with me? Now I was starting to freak out.

I woke up one of my friends and asked her if she could go to the infirmary with me. I needed to get checked out. She too was upset, because if this did happen, it would be rape. When we got there, I told the nurse what had happened; she stated that I was the third girl in there this morning, with the same issues and wondered if something was put in the drinks we had. She ran a test on me. I was good; she said, "You are the only one that shows no signs of contact, you were lucky." Could that guy really have meant what he said, that he was interested in me and made sure I got home safely?

I think to myself - *it's time for me to slow down on the partying after this has happened. I need to remember that I also have a job now at the Army base. There is no need to put that in jeopardy.* However, I didn't slow down on the drinks; every weekend, I had a six pack of something. If not, I was going out with someone else to get something. We were just drunk girls in the hallway having fun and dancing, talking bad about the boys... until one of the girls said, "Let's go to the Army base to a party." "Well, it's been a while since I have gone out, let's go," I replied.

We all piled up in this little car, looking our best, hair done, dresses looking sharp; you couldn't tell us that we weren't girlfriend material.

We were having a really good time, nothing out of control like the other parties that I had gone to. I noticed this Army gentleman was watching me; he didn't say anything to me, which was a bit creepy. Nevertheless, I continued to enjoy the party.

Later that week, while at work, I noticed the same guy from the party would come into my section. I had housewares and Knick-knacks. He would say he was looking for items for his sister and mother in Pennsylvania. It was my job to help; he seemed very nice, not sure what it was, but he was easy to talk to. About two weeks into him coming into the store while I worked, he finally told me his name, Pierce.

A week later, we went out. During the date, he gave me one of the items he had bought from me at the store. I was shocked, yet touched. The first thing I did was ask if he had a wife or a chick on the side, any of that nonsense. He said no that he was still looking for that just right person.

Three months went by fast; it was almost time for my Christmas break. I will be going home for three weeks, then I was hit from both angles. Pierce told me that he was leaving in a week to go to Lawton, OK. He would be there for six months to a year. I lost it. I started to cry uncontrollably; he assured me that nothing bad was going to happen between us. In my heart, I knew that was a lie just waiting to happen. Nonetheless, we hung out the rest of the day.

A week into my Christmas break, Pierce called me and said, "Keep an eye on the mailbox." I was like, "Ok, what's up?" He said there was a surprise on the way. I was getting excited. I love mail, just as much as I love surprises. A few days later, his letter arrives. *OH, MY GOODNESS!* The letter had a plane ticket in it for me to come to Lawton, OK.

Once I. got back to school, I could not wait to go since I had not seen him in weeks. He knew my school schedule, so the plane ticket was around that. I would only miss one day of class. This was great. I would get to see him; with my bags packed, off to the airport I went. I had never flown before, also never been outside the state of Virginia, so I didn't know if I was scared to fly, nervous or excited to see him.

The flight was something else, I was scared to death. When we took off, that scared me; to me, the plane was straight up. I became level, then felt at ease, only for the plane to start hitting air pockets. I knew at that very moment; I was going to die. My parents had no clue that I was doing this, so the only person would know it was me, would be Pierce. How could he tell my parents anything? He had never met them.

I became really close to God at this point. I remember what my Big Granny would say. If it is out of your control, give it to God. I closed my eyes and said, "Lord if it is your way, please let me land safely." Thankfully, we did land without a problem. It was at that point I said to myself that I would never fly again.

When I got there, a friend of his picked me up. She said that I was staying with her. I am like, "Who are you?" She went on to explain that her husband and Pierce are really good friends; I was ok with that. I didn't want to be staying with a stranger, but they still were to an extent. I watched too many scary movies to know that you are not supposed to go to a stranger's house. You may never make it out of there.

Later that afternoon, Pierce came over to the house to pick me up, I wanted to get out of the house. We went to the mall, we walked around talking about what we had been doing since we separated. I really enjoyed getting caught up. I got nervous when he started talking about meeting my family. Do. I. really want him to come to Virginia and meet my family? As we continued to walk and talk, he stopped in a jewelry store, after which the clerk handed him a bag, then we left. I was thinking to myself why did he need to go. In there? We stopped by a water fountain in the mall, he said he loved me and didn't want us to be separated again. He wanted to move me to Lawton to be with him. I couldn't believe what I was hearing right now. What is going on?

He handed me the ring and asked that question. All I could think about was, *if I say yes, he would take me away from the drama that I lived with, but what about my dad?* Ok... he is still waiting, "Yes, I will marry you," came out of my mouth with such ease. There were people everywhere, the crowd erupted with applause. I can't tell you when I was this happy, it was such a great feeling of that unconditional love.

While we were in the mall, we passed a small group of men who glanced in my direction; this set him off and the next thing I know, he had turned around and started a fight. This should have been a red flag to me but I was used to seeing this so I thought nothing of it. Soon enough, we were escorted out of the mall. While standing there calming him down, I saw a version of my mom standing right in front of me. That didn't matter. I knew I loved him.

After that, my plane tickets were coming once a month; we were planning a wedding that at this point, my parents knew nothing about.

The one thing that I was most proud of, is during this time, I didn't let my grades slip. I would do my work on the plane. Sometimes, I had to finish up school work while with him. We were making plans to stay that way, so I thought.

He would not send a plane ticket unless I mailed him a copy of my grades. If he thought he was the reason for my grades slipping, he wouldn't send a ticket. I made sure I kept my grades up.

As time progressed, it was time for our summer break. I had managed to make multiple trips to Oklahoma, without it affecting my grades or without my parents finding out, but when was I going to tell them that I was getting married, with one year of school left to go?

Summer break was beyond hard, I was working a summer job. The place my mom worked at hired me. So, you guessed it; I would spend most of my days with her. This is the first time I ever saw her at work. I thought she would be different at work, but now she had the same mood swings as always even on the job. I do feel deep down that she doesn't like me or is jealous. When her co-workers would give me a compliment on what I was doing, her response would be, "I do the same job; you never say anything to me." I was feeling a little uncomfortable but nonetheless, I wanted the money to pay for this wedding, which no one on my side of the family knew about.

I always looked forward to Friday and Saturday nights; that's when Pierce would call me, he said that his boys were all out partying, so he would spend that time with me on the phone because I was the one, he was with. It was a great summer. I noticed that being with him, I was never drinking or going out to parties. I would work, go home and look at wedding books. I was so happy, but I didn't know that this happiness would soon come to an end.

I came home from work one afternoon and I noticed that my mom looked like she had been crying. I asked her what was wrong and she told me to go see my dad. I walked into my dad's bedroom and he was sitting in the dark. "Hey Daddy, what's going on?"

He turned to me with bloodshot eyes, "Your Papa died today."

"NO, NO!" I screamed. "How is this possible? I just saw him two days ago; at the hospital he was fine!" "After you left," Dad said, "he started to get delirious, not knowing where he was, he wanted to go home." The doctors had the bed rails up and he tried to climb out to go home.

He fell and hit his head; that elevated his other issues and he died this afternoon. I sat next to my dad in silence. I knew that this would make my mother upset; at this time, it wasn't about her. We sat there for about an hour, before either of us said anything. I told him that I was going to pack a bag and would stay with granny while we get this taken care of.

As we prepared to bury my grandfather, I went to the funeral home, sat with him and talked to him. I asked him what I should do. I couldn't see myself going back to school, with my heart as heavy as it was. *How can I focus? How will I go on without you? Who will make sure I have enough toilet paper? Who?*

The tears burned my face with every question I had for him. As I

PAMELA JAMES COLEMAN | 154

was getting ready to leave, the funeral home, I reached over to touch his hand one last time. On the left side of his face, the entire side was black and blue. The undertakers tried to cover it with make-up, but I still saw it. I fell over him and cried. I soon felt a hand on my shoulder, asking me if I was ok.

It was my brother. I turned to him and fell into his chest, asking him why this happened to him. "Why is everything good in our life taken away? What have I ever done to continue to feel pain like this? Will this ever stop?" At this point, I am pounding his chest.

The following day, It was time for the services; it was a simple, yet nice service. Soon after, it was time for the family to view the body. When it was my turn, I passed out. We are not sure why I passed out; it wasn't like I hadn't seen him just the other day in the same way. As always, my brother was there to catch me.

Two weeks after the funeral. Summer was coming to an end, time for me to complete my senior year. I was struggling with the death of grandfather; would I be able to focus? I asked my parents if I could sit out a year. They both said "No!" We have gone through a lot to get the money for you to go back. To help with the loss of my grandfather, my parents let me live off campus and I could take my car back. Back on campus, for my final year, I was all moved in; I had a small room in a large house. The owner took one large room and split it down the middle. That was fine; I had room for my bed, dresser and a desk. I didn't need much more. All the girls had made it back to school and it was time to register for our classes. We had plans to go to the beach for the Labor Day weekend, so we were all in a rush to get through the line for registration.

My senior year would take a turn that no one saw coming. One of our friends Kent worked in the Registrar's office; he was helping out with signing up for classes. Kent waved us over and said we could get through the line faster with him, so we all went over there (big mistake). "This is great," I said. "We will be able to go to the beach." High fives were going around. He stamped our paperwork and I asked him about my check that I had to pay for my school year. Kent replied, "Don't worry about it, they will call you for that." Boy did they ever.

We went to the beach and had a great four days away from school. Senior year, we were about to rock this out. I was going to be the first one in my family to go to college and graduate, or so I thought. there the girls are, ready to party and who was I to say no? I had not heard from Pierce in 2 months. We always go to the Army base to hang out and have fun; that's when my girls found out my secret. We soon ran into one of Pierce's friends and he yelled, "Congratulations on your engagement!" The group turned to me and said, "What the hell is he talking about?" I told them that when I said I was going home for the weekend, I was really in OKC. Then the next question was "Where's the ring?" I pulled it out of my pocket and said, "Here it is. The wedding is supposed to be after my graduation."

They were excited and mad all at the same time, because I didn't tell them when it happened. I responded that my parents don't know. "WHHHAAAAATTTTT??" was said in unison. I replied "Yes, they do not know." On top of that, he has gone missing for 30 to

40 days. I am not sure what is going on.

I was noticing that my calls from Pierce started to get less by the week. I called Angela, the wife of Pierce's friend; she said that he had been acting very strange, not coming over or hanging out with her husband. So, we both started to worry, I still continued to plan a wedding. This time I told my parents. I think the roof came off the house. With the comments that you hadn't finished school yet, how long have you known him, etc. Soon, they began to come around, but as they came around, he began to fade; weeks went by with no contact, so everything I was working on, I stopped.

Thanksgiving break eventually arrived; now we have three months of no contact, no calls. After dinner, everyone went into their rooms to leave my mother alone. It was wise; that way the house would stay peaceful. The next day, my phone rang. I answered it, it was Pierce... remember it has been almost three months since the last time I saw or talked to him. *"The nerve"* I thought to myself. I asked, "What do you want?" He went on with, "I still want to get married; I am in Virginia and I want to come see you." "Really..."

My mother was on the other line listening; any other time I would be angry, but I really didn't care this time. My mom said, "Come on, we would be more than happy to meet you." I said, "You heard her, come on." I hung up and asked my mom if she had lost her mind. She said, "No," let's hear what he has to say and then you can make up your mind what you want to do.

I went into my room, to see what I was going to put on. I decided to look like a total bum; he didn't deserve my effort in getting cute! A few hours later, there was a knock on the door. Mom yells, "Come in." She never gets up to answer the door. UGH! There he stood in his Army Greens. I was happy to see him, but I was not going to let him see that I wanted to hear the lies that would come out of his mouth.

He talked to my parents for a while and then asked if we could go outside. I guess this is where I am going to get the story. He began, his reason for not keeping in touch with me, is because he didn't want to deal with the outside world? What did he just say? Had he become a nutcase or what? "I am not the outside world. I was the person you had planned to marry." His response was "I still do." "How the heck is that supposed to happen when you have been M.I.A, for damn near three months?"

He continued with what the voices in his head were saying. I stopped him right there. I was like, "It's time for you to go, I wish you the best, but this right here is not going to work." He continued how he wanted to take me to Allentown PA to live with his family. "Nope, not going to do it, you can call this off and take your ring back." He refused to take the ring, then he walked to the car. I began walking to the house and turned around; he was leaning against his grey Nissan, with his arms folded. As I closed the door that was the last time I was to see him.

Thanksgiving break is now over and I am back at school; my friends are fighting over who is going to be the Matron of honor, colors for dress, etc. "This is the best time to say this, there is not going to be a wedding." Everything just stopped; the room got quiet. "What do you mean there is not going to be a wedding?" they responded. For the first time, it really hit me that he was gone. I fell to the floor in tears, "I can't believe that it's really over," I said. I began to tell them the story of how he came to the house, talked to my parents, then said he couldn't be in touch with the outside world.

My girls just sat there, in shock listening to what I was telling them about the visit. Then it turned angry towards him, but they all started laughing when I said that my mother took my engagement ring and is wearing the hell out of it. My girls always have my back. "There is no need for you sitting here wondering what could have been, it's time to party," they said.

I have not gone out in almost a year; I have not had a drink in almost a year. I am a lightweight, I don't think I should. Mind over matter didn't work here. I swear before I blinked, I was at the Army Base. This is where all of the mess with Pierce started; here I am, back here again. I looked up, here comes one of my girls with this extremely tall guy in his Army Greens. I swear there is something about seeing a guy in Army Greens that just messes with my head. I could feel my face going a bit red, and he hadn't said a word.

When he spoke, his voice didn't match his body at all. It had a deep-south country sound to it. I almost laughed in his face, until I got used to it. His name, was Louis. We talked for a while, then the lights came on and the party was over. We didn't notice that we had been talking that long. He asked if he could call me. I hesitated, but gave in. I said to myself, *he is not going to call me.* One hour later, the phone rang; he said, "Let's pick up our conversation where we left off." We stayed on the phone until the sun came up. I told him that I just broke off a pending marriage and he said he was divorced, so he understood. I said "Divorced? How old are you?" He was five years older than I was. I called my mom to tell her about him. I said that he was 5 years older than I was. Her response was, "Age ain't nothing but a number, it's what you have and how you use it that counts." I was shocked she said this. I thought *hey, let's not pay attention to age.*

We started spending time together. I learned more about him or so I thought; he was telling me about himself. He was a nurse. I had never met a male nurse before; that was cool, to dare to be different. If I wanted to go home, he would drive so I wouldn't have to use my gas. My parents loved him, and so did I or so I thought. I felt so comfortable with him, that there was nothing stopping me from giving myself to him. I felt like he was going to be the one. Even though we had that sexual connection, I always had a feeling that something wasn't right.

I finally found out what were the red flags; there were two of them. Now that I had a car, it made it easier to get around. One day, when the girls and I were out riding, we happened to see his car parked on a strange side of town for him; he told me that he was at work.

I pulled up in front of the house where his car was and started to honk the horn until someone came out. It was Louis. I asked him what was he doing over here? He said, "Nothing, just go back to your house. I will be there in a few minutes." I looked at him and he seemed nervous about something, then a female asked him who I was. In turn, I asked the same damn question about her. She said, this better not be your wife rolling up at my house like this. I turned to him, "You said you were divorced." She yelled, "No he is still married, she is in Hawaii, where she was born. Look in his glove compartment, you will see the photos and letters she sent to him." This can't be happening; I asked her how long has she been seeing him. When she answered, I damn near passed out. She had been seeing him the same time that he started seeing me. She also added that she was just waiting for his divorce to go through so they can go public. What the hell did she just say? "Divorce", ok that's when the rest of all hell flew into me; the fool has a wife in Hawaii, that I didn't know about and a chick on the side that I didn't know about.

I got into my car and we left. Ten minutes later, he was at my house asking to let him explain. "Man please get out of my face." He apologized, and said it was hard for him to pick between the two of us. We both had qualities that he liked. I told him that he

PAMELA JAMES COLEMAN | 164

could have her. Just leave me alone, let me enjoy my last year at school. I thought I would never see him again, but the universe has a strange way of bringing people back together again.

I went home for Christmas break and there was a letter there from the school. I grabbed it, and went to my room to open it. The letter says that I was suspended from school pending an investigation of how we signed up? What do you mean, I thought it was a letter asking for the check that I am still holding onto for this semester; the letter went on to say that if I was seen on campus that I would be charged for trespassing? I couldn't let my parents see this letter. While on break, I always looked forward to eating my Grandmother's food. This year I was off and not feeling well; to see food, all I wanted to do was throw up.

My loving mother was quick to say, I hope you didn't bring one of those nasty bugs from school back home. I said, "No, I hope I didn't." "Stay away from me," she replied. I had a red sweater dress that I loved to wear during the Christmas holidays. This time, when I put it on, it didn't fit like it used to. I hadn't been eating that much. Why is there a pudge? What is going on? To avoid bringing attention to this from my mother, I took the dress off. I didn't feel like hearing the comments of getting fat. I just wanted to enjoy my holidays at home, away from the drama called Louis, his wife and the two side chicks.

When I get back to school, I told my crew to look at my belly. Their eyes grew big, then they asked "When was the last time you had a cycle?" I responded, "With all this shit going on with him I hadn't paid any attention to it." One of my girls said, "You are pregnant." "No, No, hell no, I can't be." One of them went to the store to get a pregnancy test. When she came back with it, I was scared to death. I went into the bathroom to take the test. When the time was up, I refused to go back into the bathroom to see what it said. One of my girls went in, she returned in tears. I was pregnant.

This could not be happening. I have been kicked out of school; I was seeing a darn married man (in my defense I didn't know) with two chicks on the side. Now, I am the one that's pregnant? Who did I piss off in a former life for this to happen? My girl, Tanya, picked up the phone and called Louis. She told him to get his ass over to the house right now. She didn't care if he was working with the other woman, get here now. If he wasn't there in 30minutes, she would call again. He was there in 25 minutes. When he arrived, I was in a heap just crying my eyes out. I can't say that this was all his fault, because I was there also. What I can say is, had he been open and honest with me, I am pretty damn sure this wouldn't be what we are talking about.

Louis was beyond happy; I was completely terrified. *Have you seen my mother? Have you seen the size of this woman? You have never met the raft of her anger like I have. If I brought this to her, she would kill me after I had the baby.* The next day, I had to break the rules a little; I went to the infirmary to talk to the nurse. I told her how my mother was, and what I thought she would do to me if she knew. I will always remember this lady; she sat down with me. She listened to the entire story of how we got here. Then she started to go over my options. I made a choice at that moment that I have wished many times over that I didn't pick it. I decided to end life.

When the day came, it was one of the hardest I things I have faced even with my mother's treatment; nothing will ever prepare you for this. I got undressed, put on a medical gown and I laid on the cold table. My friends, and Louis were outside for support, I still felt all alone. One by one, the doctor put my feet into the stirrups. With each lift, he would ask me if I was sure; each time he asked, I cried more. When I turned my head as I was second guessing this choice, I saw my mother in the corner of the room with her hand raised to the air. I blinked a few times and looked again. She was gone, I looked at the doctor and said, "Yes, I am sure."

Then a loud machine turned on; the doctor looked over at me while the nurse held my hand. You will feel a pinch for a few minutes, hold still. That's when I started to cry uncontrollably. *What have I done, what am I doing? Am I still that scared of my mother that I can't stand up for myself? This will forever haunt me.*

CHAPTER 2

WHEN IT WAS DONE, Louis came in to tell me how sorry he was and that this shouldn't happen to me. I yelled at the top of my lungs for him to leave. "Never speak to me again, forget I was ever a part of your life, just like this baby. Leave!" I never saw him again. I had lost a child, as well as a lying two or three timing jerk.

I was soon back in my little room at the house. Now, I was trying to figure out how I was going to tell my parents about not being in school, and what happened. I think that I had been through enough and decided not to tell them about being kicked out of school. When my dad sent the money for school, I decided to get my real estate license. The only class for that was 35 minutes away. I signed up for it and was going regularly. I would study by the area's riverfront. It was great, but, just like any of my school years, I met a group there who liked to party.

I thought I was away from this, but here again, I found myself back on the scene, in a new city where no one knew me. It was great, so great that I missed too many classes and they kicked me out with no refund.

A few months later, I decided to tell my parents that I was not going to graduate this year as planned, but how was I going to tell them this? I pulled up to the house and sat in the car for a few minutes; the plan came to me like a ton of bricks. I can pull this one off, yes, a brilliant idea.

"Hello everyone, I am home!" From the kitchen, my mother said, "We kinda figured that the way you are yelling." I yelled back,

"Hey Mom, can you come here for a minute please?" She came out of the kitchen, "What is it now?" I called my dad in and mom said, "You better not be pregnant!" That hit hard, but I had to hold back the tears. No, I am not pregnant, but I need to talk to you all about school. I was told before leaving that I am or will be short credits needed to graduate. I didn't want you two inviting people and I am not going to be walking across the stage.

It was silent for what seemed like an hour. My dad said "These things happen, you are more than welcome to stay." I was getting excited, but he hadn't finished yet. "But you will pay for the classes needed plus your room and board. I signed up to help you for 4 years, my time is done." When I looked to my right, she was livid. I braced myself for what was coming; she turned and walked away. *WHAT! Is this all I am going to get? Don't play that reverse psychology shit with me. I am the Queen of it!* My dad grabbed my arm and said, "Let it go. It will be the best thing for all of us." During my week there, she said very little to me; everything she said was directly at me.

I had made it through what I thought was going to be hard. No need to tell them I got kicked out of college for something stupid if I can just spare them the hardship. As I was going out of the door, I was saying my good-byes; my mother looked up from her puzzle book and said, "You disappoint me." Feeling heartbroken and alone, I drove back to school to college to hang out with my friends until school was over. Since my room at the house on campus was paid for until school was out. And not on campus so I wouldn't be charged with trespassing.

With everything I had gone through, I was back to being that same girl I was when I started school. If someone said party, I was there. I had learned a few things, not to take drinks from people, and how much is too much. I want to always know how I can make it home. The drinking started to cut back; I knew when I got home, this type of fun or partying was nowhere to be found.

It was hard to say goodbye to my friends, for a few reasons. I would miss them, as well as the partying that went with them. But it is time to move on.

After College

I had moved back home with my parents. I needed to get a job and figure out what I wanted to do with my life. I went to a temp agency, to have my own money, so I didn't have to ask Dad for money to do the things I may want to do, and hear backlash from Mom.

You would not believe some of the jobs that I got. The craziest one was wiping semen off of test tubes for this testing clinic. Once I found out what I was doing, that was the first and last day. EW! I didn't care that it was double per hour than the other jobs, even if it kept change in my pockets.

I took the phone bill and paid that and I cooked on Wednesday; it was spaghetti day. Dad loved my cooking, I learnt from the best. Saturdays, when they would go grocery shopping, which brought my own, I would clean the house for them.

One mid-week day, there was a knock on the door; I opened it, there stood a police officer. He asked who I was and I told him, he gave me a piece of paper. It was a warrant. *It has all caught up with me now, what am I going to do?* I went in the bedroom where my dad was lying down on the bed reading his newspaper and I sat there for a moment, then the tears just starting rolling down my face. I knew once he heard this, I will crush him, let him down and just a big disappointment to him.

"Dad?" I said. "What's up Pooh?" "I messed up, I messed up big time," I replied. "Ok what happened?" he asked. I relived the entire school year to him and what had happened, how, what, when and why. He looked at me and calmly said, "This is your mess; you did it, so now you need to figure out what is next." I am not taking off from work to get this straight. Then you could hear footsteps coming from the kitchen. *Could the floor please open up so I can go through it?* It didn't happen, she walked in, no 'hello, hey how are you doing', just straight to the point. "What the hell is going on in here?"

Well I guess I had to tell her. When I did, again, the roof blew off the house. She started going in on me, before she even got the story. She just assumed that I was in the wrong. My dad told me to go the magistrate's office, turn myself in and we will go from there. The good thing about going there, if there was a good thing, was, my dad worked there in the evenings as a janitor. So they knew who I was, because I would come down there to help my dad, just to get out the house.

When I arrived there, the man behind the desk said he was waiting for me. My dad had called and told him I was on the way. He was so nice; he told me everything that was or should happen, and that I needed a lawyer. Oh my! Where was I going to get one of these? And then it hit me. The lady that my Grandmother and I worked for when I was a tyke, was a lawyer. Her only son followed in her footsteps. Yes, I am going to see him. I went to his office to make an appointment; when he saw me, he just called me on back. I told him everything just like it happened. When I finished, he said that this could be sticky or it could be one we can walk away from. Either way, before I got back home, I had a lawyer that was on the case.

He recommended that I have no contact with any of the people that was involved, keep my nose clean, no parties, no late nights. All he wanted me to do was go to work and come home until this was taken care of. July came, the phone rang; it was my lawyer with a court date. He said, "This is going to start the proceedings, I need you to be upfront and strong. I remember my dad said he wasn't taking any days off to fool with this miss, so in the bedroom, I went to tell them the latest and ask my mother if she would mind going with me next week.

All I could think about was how long of a ride this was going to be. With her telling me what a disappointment I was, and what the hell was I thinking, so on and so forth, well, she agreed to go with me. Please tell me why she was wearing all black? No one had died. So, off we went for the hour-long ride. It wasn't held in the city that I went to school; due to the nature of the crime, it was held in a metropolitan city.

We pulled up and, to my surprise, she didn't say anything but, "Keep your head held high. "IF" you didn't do anything wrong, everything will work out fine." *What, "IF"? Hell, I have told you over and over again I didn't do anything wrong.* Never mind this, I saw my lawyer; he had a strange look on his face. He asked my mom to sit in the hallway and not the courtroom. This didn't sound good at all.

I followed my lawyer; I could feel myself shaking and ready to pass out, but that didn't happen. The door to an office opened up and there sat four people I had never seen before and a lady taking notes, I think.

They were all nice and stood up to greet me. Now I was really confused. I looked at my lawyer; he said, "You have two options, tell them everything that happened, with names and be willing to testify against the person that signed the paperwork, you walk out with no court appearance, nothing on your record, you are clear. Or you can 'not say anything, we set a court date and you take your chances on a jury believing you or not.'"

I didn't know if a choir music was playing in the background, but this girl sang so loud, I know my daddy heard me. As I was telling my story they stopped me half way in, one of them said, "Excuse me, but did you say you had the payment for the school?" I pulled the check out, dated three days before this took place. Next came, "So you were not trying to cheat the system or the school?" "Nah man I was taking a short cut to get to the beach, to have some fun. We all went to his line because he said he could get us through the line faster." I am still looking dumb. "So what is the problem? Am I in deeper trouble now?"

The District Attorney said, "No just the opposite, are you willing to tell us who signed your paperwork?" "Heck yeah if gets me out of this mess." The DA said "Well yes ma'am it would". I wrote down what he needed to know; he signed my paperwork; my lawyer and I shook his hand and we left the room. As we were leaving, one of the girls that was with me was walking into the big room. We did the head nod and kept it moving. I didn't know whether to jump for joy, cry, scream or all of the above and at that very moment, the guy that signed my paperwork, walked past me in shackles, and my joy quickly left me. All I wanted to do now was go home and forget this mess.

On the ride back home, what I was expecting going to court, was what I got going home. "How could you be so dumb, what was at the beach so important that you couldn't stand in line like you were supposed to?" Those type of questions went on for the entire hour back home. When we got home, I was like a little kid when I saw my dad. I ran up to him, told him it was all over. I got a pat on the back because my dad is not a hugger, and he said, "Good job, I hope you learned something from this, let's not do this again ok?"

Here we go, drama is coming, "WHAT!!! Is that all you got to say?" My dad was like, you need to calm down, everything worked out; we don't need to dwell on what could have happened." Oh, hell here it comes. She stomps into the kitchen and starts to blast Al Green. I knew we (my dad and I) were going to catch it now.

I wasn't sure why she was so upset; we just spent the entire day together. Here we go; if she is not the center of attention, everyone in her path would catch hell just like a tornado. Well I was right, our dinner was a can of pork n beans, and fish sticks that looked like they just ran through the over. Our plates were slammed down on the table and she puffed off to the living room to watch TV.

My dad and I ate in silence, fearing that if we had a conversation, it would hit the fan again. The door opened; it was my brother, I happy to see him. He works at a grocery store and he is always dressed like he is going to a funeral. He spoke to Mom, and headed our way, because his room was next to the kitchen. He looked like he was going to say something to us; my dad and I shook our heads 'no'. He knew what was up.

After dinner, everyone went into their rooms and left her alone; it was wise, that way the house would stay peaceful. While in my room I starting thinking about Labor Day weekend.

Labor Day weekend was close. I wanted to go back to the beach that we all hung out at for Labor Day when I was in school. My high school friend was at home and said, "Let's roll to the beach." We piled into her car and headed off to the beach. The first couple of days were great; we partied and hung out with my friends that lived in the area. It was now the last night at the beach, time to spend the day there. Something didn't feel right; there were more people than it had been in the past. There was a lot of tension and you could feel it.

Someone said that something happened the night before that had set off the black community. Of course, you hear people talking all the time; we didn't pay any attention to that person, and proceeded to the beach. I don' t think that we had been there two hours having fun, but you could hear like a wave coming towards the beach. People fighting, in groups, jumping people, yelling crazy stuff, then you started to see items flying off the balconies of the hotels. I said, "It's time to go." The sun was setting and the fights and store windows breaking were picking up speed. Streets were blocked; it took us forever to get out of there. I kept looking out the back of the window to see what was going on and it looked like a scene from a movie. You couldn't script this one at all; we finally found a side street that wasn't blocked by the police. We zoomed down that street and thought everything was good, that we were safe and could make it back to the place we were staying. NO! That didn't happen. 'POP, POP!' The back window was shot at and the entire thing came crashing down on those of us sitting in the back seat. My friend started to freak out and almost lost control of the car as she swerved; other cars dodged us, and she managed to pull over to the side of the road safely. We all got out to see what happened, but thought... *if they are shooting out here, we need to get back in the car and head back to the house.*

This had been going on for several hours; it had made all major news channels. I said to myself, *OH hell, this means daddy knows.* He watches the news at 6:00 o'clock every evening. I found the nerve to call. First it was, "Are you ok?" I replied, "Yes everything is fine, we got the window shot out." *Oops, why did that just come out of my mouth?* Both parents were on the line and they were yelling at me so loud you thought they were right there with me. My mom said, "You need to bring your ass home right now." Dad said, "What were you guys thinking driving into that mess?"

"I can't come home; I didn't drive remember? We didn't drive into the mess, it started while we were there having a good time. I will be home tomorrow; you can continue to yell at me then for something I didn't do wrong," I replied. Then you could hear my mom yelling on the other end as I was hanging up the phone on them. I said to myself, *you are rather ballsy when you are 200 miles away from home. You know all hell is going to break loose when you walk through that door.*

Oh well, the party continued; there was nothing we could do about the window now and why sit here and cry over it? We were staying at a college friend's house for the night. *Oh, Crap here comes the drinks, one after the other until I couldn't remember anything.* The next day, the sun was up and we were heading home. My girls began to pick on me all the way home. "You about to get your ass beat, your shit thrown out in the yard like that shit that was flying over the balcony." We all laughed, but in the back of my mind, I knew parts of that was oh so correct.

I was home. They kicked me out the car and said they would pray for me and drove away. I went into the house, and I could tell by the way she was sitting in her favorite chair, that all hell was going to pop off. She started on me for hanging up on her, for being rude, the list went on. Then this was the funny part. She told me to go outside and get the switches off the weeping willow tree. I looked at her, totally lost sense of what was about to come out of my mouth. I said, "You must have lost your damn mind. I am 20, if you think you are going to beat me, you are crazy." Oh shit, did all that just come out of my mouth? Please Lord, tell me I was just thinking it, and not say it.

Nope I said it, because the woman got larger than usual; there was one thing I didn't have to worry about. She wasn't going to chase me. She started throwing things at me and I took off to my room. She was yelling at me about how rude I was and that I needed to leave. I yelled back, "My brother is over 30 and you still let him live here with all the shit he does." OOPS, did it again, my mouth is like a bad fridge, can't hold nothing. I heard the footsteps heading my way. I couldn't run this time, I had to listen to her yell at me for a good 20 minutes easy, of how I was 'just like my father (Again, thank you), that I was going to end up being a trouble maker, just worthless,' she said. I put my hand over my mouth, to prevent me from saying the next thing on my mind. She raised her hand like so many times before. Her response was, "I wish you would."

You know, her statements to me used to hurt, but this time I could have cared less. My friend asked me before she went to work, if I would mind taking the car to get a price on how much it would cost to get the window fixed. "Sure, I am off today, I got you covered," I offered.

So, I took the car out to a local dealership, not thinking it was still Labor Day weekend the service area would be closed. I drove up there just to check; there was a salesperson there. Who knew that this would be the start of a change in my life? He told me that it was closed and to come back tomorrow; he then asked what happened to the car. I told him of the crazy stuff that went on and he said he heard about it on the news, "didn't think anyone from here was crazy enough to go," he continued. I said to myself, *who is this fool?* I said, "Thank you," and drove off.

With summer officially ending, I was back doing my temp jobs as well in the big box store. This time, the service placed me with a phone company; the job was to scheduled last for eight to twelve weeks. I liked this job, it was fun. I was sitting next to a young man at the phone company, that lived in the same area as my Grandmother, so we had a lot to talk about. I also made friends with this young lady in the office; we all had a lot in common. We would take lunch breaks and hang out. Stevie and I started to get close, we had fun going out. Eventually, I met his mother and sisters and we all were getting along well. Two weeks later, we got a call that Stevie had a seizure; because of this, he would need a ride to work. Soon, I started out giving him the ride to work. Little did I know that one of our mutual friends drives past his house on the way to and from work, so she soon began to pick him up. After about a month, I started to notice that he was not acting like himself. One day in the work parking lot, he told me he couldn't see me anymore; he admitted he had feelings for her and didn't want to hurt me.

Too late, I was crushed. I called my job the next day and I asked for a transfer so I would no longer be near this mess. When Stevie saw that I was no longer coming to work, he began calling me. but I wouldn't take his calls. My mother said that she was not my secretary; she said that I needed to talk to him just get it over with, or send him a message to stop calling, because she was going to tell him off. I did just that. He was in a state where he could now drive, so he came over after work and we talked for a while. He apologized for hurting me the way he did, but there was a reason. He looked at me, and said, "She is pregnant. I have to do the right thing. I am going to marry her." At that point, I said, "You can get the hell off my porch, I hope never to see you again."

The car my brother gave me was starting to act up; the brakes were going to the floor when I pushed on them. We all know that wasn't safe. I remember taking a photo of this really cool purple car that I said *if I was going to get a car, this would be the one.* I went back out to the dealership, and you know it; the same person, that was here when I was trying to fix the window, walked up to me, to help me. Jokingly, he said, "So you have a car with a window in it this time." "HAHA," I said. I told him that I needed to get a new car and this is what I would like to have.

He took the photo, ran my credit and told me that he would get back to me. The next day, he told me that for a brand-new car, I would need a co-signer and that the car I wanted was specialized and they didn't sell cars that color. I was so crapped out. I said, "Thank you," and hung up the phone.

A few days later he called back, he sounded excited. "What's going on?" I asked. He said that this weekend, they are running a special and he had just the car that would fit in my budget and no cosigner needed. I told my dad about it and he said he would help with the car, but he was not going to have one thing to do with the insurance; I was on my own. I was past excited. The special was $89.00 down and $182 a month. *Oh yes, I can handle this.*

I went out that weekend and got me the cutest little red car; I was ready to go. While at the dealership, I noticed that there was this person that would come over and sit down to talk to me while my salesperson would walk away. At first, it was ok, then it turned a little creepy. Nevertheless, I got the keys to my car and I was excited. I did my first grown thing ever. I still had some items that were owed to me, such as floor mats. He said as soon as they come in, he would bring them to me.

I had started working at this department store that was around the corner from the dealership for the holidays for extra money and now that I have this car payment, I needed to keep it, along with my temp job. I noticed one night that the other guy that was coming to the table during my purchase was now coming into the store to talk to me. He said he was shopping, but there was no way you could come in every other day, on trip four or five, he asked me out. I said yes, just to see if he would go away.

The following night, my salesman was outside when I got off from work. He said he wanted to talk to me about something, so I sat in the car with him. He was telling me of how his coworker, who asked me out, was talking about he had a date with me and plans he had that he was going to do, basically just bragging. The salesman was telling me this because he didn't want anything to happen to me. I thought that was truly nice of him to tell me, because he didn't have to.

When, it came time for the date, that same coworker was outside of my job waiting for me. I told him that he could go straight to hell. "You are not a real man to respect, if you are at work bragging about you got a date with me, and the plans you have. I want no parts of it or you. Please carry your ass away from me."

After I told his coworker to go away, Kenneth came over to check on me, he said, his coworker looks like a hot mess. Then we started hanging out, just like I would with my girls, we had fun.

Kenneth and I were out eating pizza one day and he said, "You know, I need to narrow down who I am spending my time with." I told him he was acting like my brother, not a one-woman man, so I responded, "Which one are you going to date? The one over the mountain or the one down the highway?" I told him he'll be like my brother and date them both; just don't get caught. I ended up laughing until my sides were about to bust.

He looked up from his pizza and replied, "No, I think I am going to stick with you." "WHAT!? I never thought I was in the running." We were kicking it and hanging out. He even was trying to help me plot against this guy that had dumped me. Kenneth, told me that if you put a candy bar in the gas tank instead of sugar, it will take longer to mess up the engine. Who knew right? Yet, I was still sitting there with pizza cheese hanging from my chin in shock.

I told him let's play it by ear, see what happens. So now I have been hired full time with a telephone manufacturing company. I really like the job and the people; that is how I was hired, Ms

Charming in full effect. I was excited to be a full-time employee with a steady check and insurance.

Later that day, it started to snow really hard while I was at work. My phone rang and there Kenneth was; he said, "When you are ready, I will take you home so you don't have to drive in the snow." *What? Really? Ok.* When they closed the plant, I would say less than an hour after he called, I walked outside. There he was in this jeep. I thought, *this is going to be fun*. How wrong was I. I got into the jeep; there was a hole in the floorboard and he had no heat. Ok, in my mind, I wanted to call my dad, but I didn't want anything to happen to him just because I couldn't suck it up for about 20 minutes or less to go home.

Ok I am in, let's do this. Why did he take off like some type of fool? I screamed and he said, "You will be ok, just hold on." I said, "Hold on to what? The door is made out of cloth and there are no grips in the roof of the jeep." He said, "Hold on to the roof bar if you get scared." I can say that the ride home was a good hour; I am sure it wasn't, but it felt like it. When we got to my house, he said, "Want to go riding?" "Hell no, I am cold, hungry and damn near cranky, let me out."

He came around to my side and opened the door so I could slide out and slip and slide into the house. He then yelled that he would call me later and that he wanted to talk about something. "Ok," I said, and thought to myself *what could this be about I wonder?* I ate dinner; my house was very calm. I think it was the snow that had everyone at ease. Mom had fixed brown beans and corn bread. Oh, that was so tasty, especially when it was cold outside. Now, when my mom puts her mind to it, there are some dishes she can cook. Her famous one was chicken spaghetti. When there was a party or lunch at her workplace, she always had to take that to work; everyone asked for it. I would help her fix it sometimes when she was in a good mood or wanted some help. Eventually, the phone ring I answered, "Hey, I made it home." "That's good, what's up?" I replied. "Well, I want to ask you something." My mind started to race, because I have said time and time again, he is not the type of person I would settle down with, because he smokes, one of my pet peeves all the time. Because my dad smokes, I always smelled like smoke.

"Ok, ask your question." He said, "I always go out of town once a year with friends, and I was wondering would you like to join us this year?" My response was, "When and how much?" His response was "July, no cost. I will pay for it in the Bahamas." I almost fell out, I told him I had to think about it, because I would be changing departments on July 1st and I was not sure I could leave.

When I returned to work, I asked my new supervisor if it was ok and he, like my parents, said "Don't pass up a possible once in a lifetime trip." During my lunch break, I told Kenneth I would go with. This was January; it seemed like July was here in a blink of an eye. We traveled with 3 other couples and a few friends. Overall, it was a good trip; some of the people got on my nerves, but I couldn't say anything, because they were his friends, not mine. While we were there, I remember I walked past this huge boat, and said, "I would love to be on one of those one day." We all laughed and kept going. I still wasn't really sure about this relationship if that's what it was,

One Friday night, Kenneth and I had gotten into playing this one video game at his house, we were determined to beat it. We started at 8:00pm and the next thing I knew, the sun was up. *Oh Shit, I know I am going to hear about this.* I left and went home; as soon as I walked through the door, wholly hell broke loose. "Where have you been? I have been sitting in this chair all night worrying about you. You couldn't have called or something." From the bedroom, I heard my dad say, "She is lying! She has been sleeping the entire night. She just got in that chair when she heard your car pull up." The door opened again; it was my brother. He was like. "Hey, good morning, how is everyone?" WHAT? "Wait………. how can he just stroll in here and say what's up and I get a rash of shit?" The response was, "He is 11 years older than you, he is a boy/man and we told him that if he wasn't going to come home before 10:00pm, don't, because when you open the front door, the lock pops and wakes us up." "OKKKKKKKKKKK, so again I say, why are you jumping on me?"

It got really quiet. I said, "I would like the same rules, because when I leave, I always respect you and tell you where I am at." I was shocked; I thought I would get a bunch of crap, but I didn't. They agreed on it. My mom, not so much, but was ok. Things were back to normal. They went to the grocery store, I cleaned the house and waited for Kenneth to get off from work so we could hang out.

This went on for a while; my parents and grandparents were just taken by him. In their eyes, there was nothing he could do wrong. When we decided to get a house together, the shit hit the fan. My mother and Grandmother handed it to me that I wasn't raised to be a loose woman, and to shack up with someone, insisting that if I was going to do this, I needed to be married. Can you believe they both agreed on something for once? I didn't listen to them at all. We went ahead to get the place we wanted, but we didn't qualify for it.

I was beyond crushed; I knew that this was going to be my ticket out of this house, I could do things the way I wanted to and didn't have to hear about it. Or would I?

When that fell through, he knew that I was very sad about it, so he picked me up from my house and handed me an envelope. It was two tickets for a Cruise; I almost passed out. He said, "Since we couldn't get the house, maybe this would help ease the pain." Oh, did it ever! Forget about the house, now I was focused on the adventure.

We were going on a cruise in November. I was so excited again and didn't know what to pack, but our travel agent, who was my gossip buddy at work, gave me the itinerary for the cruise so that I was able to pack what I needed.

When we got to the ship, and walked on, it was huge; I had never ever seen anything like this. When I tell you, I took over 200 pictures. I knew I would probably never experience anything like this again and I wanted to remember it all. I was having the time of my life; there was a show that I wanted to see that had one of my favorite actors in it. We sat down and I ordered a beverage, because he didn't drink. You will find out why later, but this girl can throw them back. The show was amazing. I went to reach for my glass and there was a ring box sitting next to my drink. I turned around and he said, "Open it." There it was, a beautiful diamond ring. I turned to him and of course, I said 'YES!'

When we went to dinner that night with our table guest, they looked at my hand and saw the ring that wasn't there the night before. I was really looking forward to telling Mom and Dad when I got home; how excited and surprised they are going to be. Or will they? When the trip came to an end, I was heading home to tell Mom and Dad; I got in the house and Mom was in the kitchen, so I said to myself, *you know how she is... if you tell Dad before her, the shit is going to hit the fan.*

"Mom, I got something to tell you," I said, sounding like a little kid at Christmas. She turned to me and said, "You got engaged on the ship, let me she the ring." "WHAT THE HELL! How did you know? Why couldn't you play along even if you did know? Why did you feel the need to steal that moment from me?"

I couldn't get any madder, or so I thought. She said, "The girl that works with him at the dealership told me at the hair salon. Everyone there heard her and was so excited for me." "YOU? Why you? You didn't get the ring... you already got one of my rings!" I was pissed. I walked off without showing her the ring. I got back in my car and drove to his house to tell him of the shady shit his friend did and how hurt I was.

He told me to calm down, that it wasn't that big of a deal. "Bullshit," I said. "When I see her, I am going to let her know about it." it was only 3 days before I would bump into her. I gave her not a piece, but my entire thoughts on how she messed up what was my one and only time to share something nice with my parents. She had no remorse and told me that I needed to get over it. "NOT happening lady, you will be sorry you messed with the wrong person."

A date had been set and things were starting to get underway for the wedding of my "dreams". I was getting out of the house and was going to look absolutely beautiful- my dad said. I told him, "I hope so." We were laughing. He was happy, because he didn't have to pay for the wedding. We paid for everything ourselves.

I was looking for my wedding dress, but I couldn't find one that was in my price range; in addition, one of my bridesmaids said she couldn't afford her dress for the wedding. We came up with a great idea. She was getting divorced from her husband so she no longer wanted anything to do with the dress, so I said let me pay for your dress for the wedding and I will take your gown. That seemed like the perfect thing to do in my book, right? No, when I shared our plan with the future husband, he said, "No, this is not going to happen this way. That dress is bad luck and I don't want you to have any parts of it."

I said, "Ok." I took her dress anyway; he never saw it, so what difference would it make? The wedding drama didn't stop there. My Little Grandmother, God bless her, still stuck in her ways, first of all complained about the color of my bridal party dresses. We were getting married at night, so I thought the black and white dresses would be beautiful. "Oh no," she said, "You can't have that color, this is not a funeral." Ok, so I changed the dresses to forest green. Then this one was the most shocking; my maid of honor was white, so was one of my bridesmaids. She asked me if I had any other friends that I could put in the wedding. She had friends coming and she didn't want to be embarrassed? "What? This is my wedding, not yours and no, I am going to keep them in there." She went on to say, "I need them to make sure they do something to their hair, you know how greasy it gets." WHAT the hell? We are not back in the slave years.

I was telling Kenneth about this and he said, "I got good news for you." "Ok, I could use some right about now. What is it?" The dealership would like to offer us the showroom for the reception. I thought that was different; it was all glass and at night, that would be great. Oh lord, her comments on that, my Grandmother complained just about everything that I was doing with the wedding.

Fast forward, the year went by fast and here we were on the day of the wedding. My prayers were to let everything go ok and for those that have given me grief, behave until I come back from my honeymoon. Picture this. For November, it was a warm and beautiful day; the dealership had let us use a brand-new black car of some sort with a sunroof. Who cares? We were having a great time and me and one of my bridesmaids were heading to the church, but took the long way there. She was hanging out of the sunroof waving at people, what a blast.

I pulled in front of the church and people were going in; the rest of my girls were running out toward me. "Where the hell have you been?" they asked. "What do you mean?" I replied. They said, "You have 15 minutes to get ready." I didn't know we had taken that much time on the long route here. They said that the future husband couldn't wait. "He walked here in his Tuxedo and has been here an hour," they continued. *Not my fault he is in a rush.* We got downstairs and they were shoving me in my dress; one of the bridesmaids had grabbed a handful of my breast to adjust in the dress. I was like, "Whoa, too personal and you are in my space; those people upstairs are not going anywhere, stop rushing me."

Finally, I was dressed and ready to go; the doors closed after everyone had walked in and there stood me and my best friend, the one that has protected me all of these years my father. I turn to my dad and said, "I can't do this." With his big brown eyes, he grabbed my arm and said, "Pooh, I paid $89.00 for this monkey suit you got me in. The same people that are in there for your wedding, will be the same people that will show up for your funeral. So which one is it going to be?"

I wanted to laugh, but I wasn't sure if he was serious or not. I took a deep breath, the doors opened and the guests stood. Some of them waved as I walked by, while others were crying, as some just seemed shocked. When I got to the front, my fiancé was all smiles. I looked over at my mother and she was crying like I was dead. My Grandmother was rolling her eyes; all I could do was say "What a hot mess."

When it was time for dad to sit down, we had to tell him he could leave now, which brought about a chuckle. After the vows, exchanges and prayers, when the preacher was done and said, "You may now salute your bride," we both did the military salute, which again brought more chuckles. As I turned, I remembered that *it didn't matter that this day was about you, show her the attention*. Before we walked back down the aisle, I leaned over to my mom and gave her a kiss and said, "Thank you." Did I have to do it? No. Did I want to? Parts of me... yes. Everything was going good, photos were being taken, my Grandmother was grumbling over to the side how long it was taking and my mom was eating this up.

We finished with the photos and we made our way to the dealership, where were met by cheers, hugs you name it. During this time, the photographer was taking photos and we were all caught up in the fun of it all. I noticed that I didn't have my purse with me; it had my tickets in it for the honeymoon cruise, as well as my money and passport. I didn't freak out, I left it to one of my girls to look for it. Little did they know what hell they were about to bring.

One of them asked my mom if she had seen it. Now, in the real world that is a yes or no answer. Nope, not a chance. My mother didn't hear "Ms., have you seen her purse?" No, she heard, "What did you do with her bag?"

OMG! How did we get here? So, we are taking photos at the cake, then I look out the window; there is my mother, she is out there just crying. At this moment, I can't go out there to fix this issue. So, we continue taking photos until it became time for the cake bite. The damn cake was burnt. Yes, you heard me, the caterer burnt my cake; someone thought I was choking and took off to get me something to drink. I said, "No this shit is burnt."

At first it was funny, then when I saw that no one was able to eat it, I was pissed, but didn't have time to deal with that. I had to go outside, to deal with my mother. I get out there and she has a group of people around her. She was crying and said that one of the girls said she had lost my purse." I told her, "She didn't say that, she asked you if you had seen it. You turned it around, I am not having this tonight of all nights. Let me ask the question, have you seen my purse, so we can move on to the next person that may have held onto it?" As she was about to answer, someone came running outside and said they found it. It was with the gifts, all is good. Yes, she had the spotlight during the reception, because everyone I passed, instead of congratulations, I got, "Is your mom ok?"

CHAPTER 3

The Marriage

WE RETURNED from our honeymoon, moved into our apartment and were having fun opening the gifts. My mom called; it started off so nice. She said she missed us and wanted to know when I was coming over. "Mom, I just got home two days ago. Give me a few days to get back to normal; I will be over." Then she said if we get double of anything, she wants it. I said "What?" She repeated, "Give me all your doubles, I know you got some really nice gifts."

I just ignored her and kept going. So now we were approaching my favorite holiday of the year, Christmas. This was our 1st tree and we got to decorate it any way we wanted to. I loved this. It was a great Christmas, no drama. Everyone was getting along and dinner at my Grandmother's house was great. We stopped by my husband's mom and dad's house and things were starting to feel normal. We both worked, so when I would get off some days, I would stop by my Mom and Dad just to say hello.

There were days I would go into the house, and a familiar sound would take me all the way back to when I was young. The music turned up loud and daddy was in the bedroom room reading his paper. On this day, since the music was cranked up so loud, she didn't hear me come in, so I stopped at the bedroom where Dad was and sat there. We were chitting and chatting, then the music went down. I thought the song had changed, but nope, she had turned it off, to return to what I guess was an argument in progress. When she came into the room, she was screaming, "Now let me tell you one thing" ... you could see my dad starting to shrink and I too was not feeling all that comfortable about what was about to come next. We didn't have an exit either; she was standing in the doorway.

I greeted her, "Hey Mom, how are you?" "You can stop to talk to your daddy, but couldn't come in to say hello to me?" "Um, Mom you were in there with your music turned up. Growing up in this house, when that is the case, you want to be left alone, so I stopped in to see what daddy was doing." Oh boy, here comes the drama I hadn't seen in a while; she looked like she could flip a bridge.

She laid me out and told me I was just like my daddy and that I could take his little ass with me. I must have had a leave of absence. I told her, "If he would leave, I would take him without a bit of hesitation." "Oh, you think because you are married, I can't whip your ass?" Dad told me to leave and that it would be ok. I said, "Really, do you remember the woman, when I was little that picked you up and threw you out the front door? That woman is still standing right here."

His response was, "I have been dealing with it for a long time now. I got it; you leave." Again, he was protecting me like he did when I was little. By now, she was back in the kitchen with the music cranked up. I went home; I was so upset and tired after dealing with my mother. I went to sleep and the next thing I knew, it was time to get up to go to work. I had slept through the afternoon into the night. I never heard my husband come home from work. As I was getting ready, I just didn't feel right. I called into work and went to the doctor.

After doing some checks at the doctor's office, Doc came back in the room with a smile on his face and told me I was pregnant. Good thing I was laying down, because I almost passed out. We are not even at our one-year anniversary yet. Once I was home, I called my job to let them know I will need a few days off. When my husband came home, I had gone to the store and got a pair of booties and put them in a grocery bag. He asked, "What did the doctor say?" I said, "He gave me a bunch of meds and I need to go back in a few days." "What did he give you?" he pressed. I said, "It's over in the grocery bag." He opened the bag up and I thought he was going to be upset, but instead, he let out a yell that the entire apartment complex could hear. I just wished we were going to be met with the same reaction from our family.

Every Sunday, we would go to my Grandmother's house. Now, I was just going with my husband in a different car. This Sunday was to be a great Sunday with everyone there, my brother and his soon to be wife and son, Mom and Dad and my Grandmother and her friend. She would get mad if you said boyfriend. We were all getting along, then my Grandmother got suspicious when I didn't drink any of our favorite sips together. It was quiet and time to bless the food. I volunteered to do it. I ended with, "May God bless the new addition to the family, Amen." You could hear a pin drop, then it started. "You have not been married a year yet. How did this happen?" I thought to myself, *please don't make me tell you?* Everyone was concerned that we would end up divorced and that our child would end up as part of a broken home.

After a few months went by, my Grandmother began to accept and grow excited about the little person. Our lives and our marriage would start to feel challenges. On my husband's side of the family, he always lived with his parents; when we got married, everyone thought that we would move into his house. I wasn't trying to be insensitive, but I wanted my own place. So we got an apartment.

I thought about it, but I wasn't ready for the medical responsibilities that went along with taking care of a baby. Fast-forward a few months, our little baby boy was born, and let me tell you... When I say he looked just like I did when I was born, it is not an understatement. My mother was there for at least 10 hours, until my husband said, "Go home and rest, we will let you know as soon as we are done." I was very happy that she was there, who would have thought that she would come to hospital, let alone stay?

After a 2-day stay in the hospital, it was time to go home; my mother told my husband that my dad would drop her off so that she could help me and the baby. What? Did I hear this correctly? She is coming to help me, WOW. The next day, the doorbell rings;

there stood my mother, ready to help me, or so I thought. She made herself comfortable. When the baby cried, she was still sitting. When he needed to be changed, she was still sitting; she even asked me, "When you get up again, can you fix us some lunch?" What the hell? I couldn't do it anymore. I told my husband, "When you get home, tell her that you are off the rest of the week. I was doing more work with her here." So my husband, let my mother know she didn't have to come over for the rest of the week and we would see them on Sunday.

After the baby's birth, my mom's outbursts seemed to calm down. She was focused on the baby when we dropped him off. She did a really good job with him; they became buddies, fast. My mom and dad were always doing something with him. Dad would take him outside with him to work in the yard. He was a little fellow at this time, so he didn't mind playing in the dirt. My mother started to become the permanent sitter, because her attitude had improved.

I was working the end of month inventory that we always have when the phone rang. I was my husband on the phone saying my daddy's was in the ER and we had to get there quick. Upon arrival, the doctors told me that my dad had a heart attack and needed open heart surgery. NO, NO! Not my dad, he is too strong for this to happen to him! As they took him away, baby boy had his arms reached out to him, "No papa, no papa..." The entire room broke down at this point.

Dad pulled through; he had 3 blocked arteries. We walked in the room and he couldn't talk, because of the tubes in his mouth; I couldn't do it. I went back later that afternoon and he was sitting up, talking and joking. This is the man I knew; he can take a hit and keep going. He has always been my rock, inspiration and protector. The doctor came in to see what my dad's set up was at home and I told him he can't go home; I need him in a rehab center so that when he returned, he could take care of himself like he used to.

That didn't go over well with my mother. She stood up and asked who was he married to? I turned to her and asked, "Are you going to be able to get him his bath, meds, teach him how to walk again? NO, so I am sending him there." My dad chimed in, "I want to go there." My mother stomped out of the room. That's when we all saw glimmers of the old her returning. Dad bounced back was his normal self, still smoking, didn't learn much from it. His statement, "I got to die from something."

While I was dealing with my hard-headed dad, Kenneth was dealing with his mom memory issues and Kenneth dad was having a hard time with it. His dad would always call him and Kenneth would leave at the drop of a hat. This is where I was starting to notice that I had picked up some of my mom's bad habits. When Kenneth would say he was leaving to go help them, I would get very quiet and nod my head. I thought to myself, *you are acting like your mother; when things didn't go the way she wanted, she would show off.* I can't do this; I can't travel down this road. As soon as the garage door would close, and the baby was asleep, I would grab something to drink to level out the feelings I had inside. As the year went on, I did offer to help with ideas on how to make it easier for the family. One day, Kenneth's mom wanted to go home, yes, she was at her house, but she didn't see it as hers. I told them to put her in the car and take her for a ride; she will be fine. That worked. Momma C, my husband's mother, would see people in the closet and instead of people around her agreeing, they said nothing was there; then she would get upset. I would go upstairs, talk to the 'people' until she told me that they were gone. A year of this went on, before we got the call that my husband's mother had died.

It was hard for him, because he was truly a momma's boy. I was trying to support him during this, while my mom was pulling at me; she stated, "You see, you need to spend more time with me, you never know what might happen." I was shocked that she was thinking of herself at this time of loss. My dad and my brother were there with her, how much more attention did she need? We soon had family members asking if we were moving his dad in with us.

Again, *I can't handle those responsibilities, it is not that I don't love and care for my husband's father I am not ready to walk into the house and find him dead. I don't want to expose my kids to that kind of life.* There I was feeling signs of my mother in me coming to rear its head. I had a very hard time with my husband leaving every time the phone rang when his two sisters and his brother were here. His dad never called them; Instead, his dad would always to come to him for help with whatever the problem was. There were times I would worry that he would lose his job, because he would sneak out when Kenneth's dad called and try to make it back before anyone noticed. I know it was very selfish of me to act this way; some of it was what I had seen all my life, the other was, he just wasn't at home. I would soon understand the responsibilities.

The same month my husband's mother died, I found out I was pregnant again. This was a distraction to all that was going on in our lives right now. The news of another one coming into the family was different this time. We had been married for 5 years now; the family felt we were in a solid commitment, and our first son wouldn't be a product of a broken home.

Fast-forward a few months, the time was here to deliver; it was a Saturday morning when all of this started. At my dad's house, nothing had changed; they were at the grocery store. James was so excited that his brother or sister was on the way. He didn't want to stay with my mom; he wanted to go with us. I told him, "As soon as the baby gets here, your dad will come pick you up."

That seemed to calm him down a lot. Mom and Dad, finally returned and James ran to my mom, Nana, "Nana we are having a baby." We all laughed; 12 hours later, we were blessed with another sweet baby boy. His older brother loved him so much that he spent the first six months sleeping in the room with us. He always wanted to hold him, change him and take him out the crib.

I was very busy, as Randall was born 20 days before Christmas, and by the time Christmas rolled around, postpartum had kicked in. When my husband went to work on the 26th, I pushed the tree over, I opened the deck door, threw the Christmas tree with ornaments over the deck and watched it roll down the hill. The ornaments went flying everywhere. I really didn't know at the time what was wrong with me.

When Kenneth came home, the house was back to normal; he looked around and saw the kids were happy and there I sat on the sofa crying my eyes out. He sat next to me and asked, are you ok? Where's the tree. The entire time, all I could think about was *would a drink help me or hurt me? If I did drink, would my kids be ok?* Then I really started to cry, because if I could sit here and think about what would happen to my babies if I drank, why in the hell couldn't my mother think of the same things?

Looking at my kids, I just sat there for a moment, relieved everything, how she treated me and why she would do this, I didn't want to be like her. I wanted nothing to be like her. As the kids started to grow up, I made sure that they got to see both of my Grandmothers, to see what a blessing they are to have. The boys always looked forward to seeing my Big Granny; she always had a tin of sugar cookies ready for them when they got there and a story about me to tell.

When we would visit Little Granny, she had that huge yard where they could run, play and do things that kids love to do.

Living in the country, Little Granny also got them a sand box. When I was there, there were 4 ply boards in a square with sand; now my kids have a plastic turtle with sand and sand toys. My dad would get a chair and sit outside with them and leave us in the house. I didn't mind; they got time to hang out with Daddy, and I think he wanted to get away from Mom.

Mom was her normal self; she was over on the butcher's block eating the sweets. My Grandmother said, "That is for after dinner." She huffed, and walked away. Who knew that eating all those sweets would come back to haunt her?

As the boys got older, my youngest started to act differently when it came time to go to my mom's house on Fridays. He would ask, can we just go home? I said, "You know she has ordered pizza for you guys; I promise I won't be long, I am going to the store and will come right back, ok?" He agreed. As time went by, it became more frequent. If my dad wasn't in the yard when I pulled up, Edmond wasn't going in.

One day, I really didn't have anything to do, so I hung around just to see what was going on. My heart broke. I thought she was past her ways of being selfish. My youngest would go out with my dad; he liked the outside and my oldest enjoyed the old TV shows that Mom watched. This would be a good thing, right? They each had a grandson to hang out with them. NOT! When the youngest returned inside, she gave him grief like she did me when I paid attention to my father.

I told her that she shouldn't do that. "He likes the outside; it's not picking one or the other, that's just who he is." It stopped for a while and he was ok with going over. A month or so later, they both started to not want to go see my parents. I asked my oldest what was going on. He said that "NANA fights with PAPA. We don't like to hear it."

I was taken all the way back to kindergarten. I told them both I was so sorry that they had to see that. I explained that I grew up in that and I promised to never let them experience something like that ever. "That is why you don't hear me and your father have issues." The visits started to slow down; sometimes I would stay and keep the visits short, so that everyone was comfortable.

My mom, being a large lady, we/I would have to cut her toe nails because she couldn't reach down to get them. One day, they looked super long, so I took the day off from work and we went to get our toes done. I thought that would be a good thing. As soon as she walked in, the smell started her breathing issues up. The employees handed her a mask, which we thought made everything better. My mom had a bunion on the side of her foot; the foot tech shaved it down, but it started to bleed. We put a band-aide on it in hopes it would stop.

A few days later, it was still bleeding, so we took her to the ER. The doctors came out to explain she has something serious going on and they would have to admit her. We all went up to the room and we waited for the doctors to come in. Never in a million years would we expect this; they would have to remove part of her leg due to severe Diabetes. The room grew very quiet, and then it happened. "This is all your fault!" pointing to me. "If you had just got on your ass and cut my toe nails yourself, we wouldn't be here." I started to cry, "You took me to that place, they messed up my foot, now I am going to lose it and it is all your fault. Get out and don't ever come back." I ran out. There are times I wished I had listened to her, and never came back.

I went back the next day before the surgery and braced for the drama that I hadn't seen in a while to hit me. When I opened the door, she asked "Where have you been?" I told her that "You kicked me out, you blamed me, told me to never come back." Her response was 'she was just playing.' *What the hell, are you nuts? Who plays like that?* When the doctor came in, he said he was glad to see me. My mom, in turn, said, "Oh you know the person responsible for this." Heartbreak again. This is what I had to live with for the rest of my life. Her surgery went well; she spent a good amount of time in rehab. My dad, on the other hand, was like a kid in the candy shop. The house was clean; there was somewhere to sit. Previously, my mom always kept junk all over the place. Now, there were no dishes in the sink and he was cooking.

I had never seen him happier or less stressed. I asked if he was ok, his response, "Never better." He asked if I had checked on my Big Granny, that she hadn't seemed herself when he went down there." I replied, "No I haven't, but I will go check now."

Big Granny was a block or two from Dad's, walking distance. That was one of the things she always said she didn't understand, is why my mom wouldn't come see her, if she was only a block away. I had no answers for that. When I got there, in front of her house was an ambulance. I thought it was for the neighbor next door, but as I got closer, it was my Big Granny being rolled out. She couldn't breathe and they thought she was having a heart attack.

I went with them; she had no one really to go and I was there. The Doctor said that she had multiple things going on with her health and she was starting to decline. I was there alone and all I could do was cry. He said, "There's no time frame; she just needs to be around someone that can care for her 24 hours a day."

During this time, dealing with my mother's loss of limb, we had to take my sweet Big Grandmother to a nursing facility. She started having medical issues that did not allow her to stay at home alone. She enjoyed the nurses that were there to take care of her, the stories she would share and the nurses looked forward to seeing her. During her stay there, my Grandmother made a few more trips back and forth to the hospital. When I got the call, they told me that this may be her last trip.

During all of this, my mom had returned home; she refused to use her prosthetic leg to learn how to walk again. There was always an excuse as to why she wouldn't use her "fake" leg. At this point, she had three of them sitting in a corner holding video tapes and beauty products.

Her actions became stressful on my dad. He was now cooking dinner for them both and bringing it to her on a tray. You could see that it was taking a toll on my dad. I stopped in to tell my mom about her mother and what was going on. She told me to handle it, like I have been doing everything; my feelings were hurt. I thought she would want to be involved, but as always, it was back on me.

We got to the hospital and my Big Granny was hooked up to the ventilator to help her breathe. I called my brother, and her niece in Maryland. The doctor told me that she was gone and the only thing that was keeping her alive was the ventilator. It was up to me to make the call to take her; no one else wanted to do this. I eventually signed the papers to end my Grandmother's life. To me, I killed her and no one else could tell me any different.

My brother and I went to the house to break the news to my mom and Dad that she was no longer with us. My mom started to tear up a little, and then she turned to ask what I was going to do about her items. Really? Is that what we are doing at this moment? I did my best to give my mom a say so in the funeral planning. She picked out the dress for her home-going, and the rest was left up to me and her niece. My brother and his girlfriend did the program.

Since Mom didn't transfer from chair to car, we had to get

transportation that could get her there. Once there, she had the fight, the breakdown, I didn't get it. Was this real emotion or another production of hers? We let her have her show. After the services, she went home. We all gathered at a home right across the street from my Grandmothers. Once everyone was gone, I took Mom and Dad some food for dinner and to check on Mom. When I got there, dad was on the phone with 911; she had fallen, now we were taking her to the hospital. I was getting tired, from the services, hosting people and now, being at the hospital. I have to go home, to take care of two kids while Kenneth was at work and go to work.

My mom's falling went on for a solid year plus; she would fall, have a trip to the hospital, 21 days in the nursing home then back home. It hadn't gotten part of a routine; this would bring all the attention to her, so we have gone from drinking and throwing people out the door, to falling, going to the hospital then to the nursing home where she would get more attention than she could handle. At the nursing home, no one was making her walk or do anything she didn't want to do. She could lay in the bed a day if she wanted to.

Mom returned home from the nursing home and was not happy with the food my dad made. There were times I would be there and she would look at me and say "Ssshhhh!" She would put the food in a napkin, then she would hide it. Mom told me that dad put too much food on her plate. One day, "Mom said something about it and dad turned to her; his response was, "If you can do better, GET UP, and help."

Oh boy! Why was I there for that exchange? Even in a wheel chair, she was able to fire off some of the nastiest words and harsh things to him. I still sit and wonder *why did he stay here?*

The attention was going to be taken away from her. My dad had a stroke; it was my dad's turn to get every ounce of attention that I had. We got daddy to the hospital in enough time to get a shot to help him return to a normal life. Now, he had to spend time in the nursing home, I knew this was the perfect time to get my mom removed from the house. I called Adult Protective Services, to help, because due to her situation, she couldn't be left alone.

She locked the door and wouldn't let them in. Furthermore, she wouldn't talk to me; the only person she would let in the house was my husband. Once in, he tried to get her out, but she wouldn't go. The only thing we could do was wait for her to fall again, then take over. Dad was in the nursing for his recovery almost two months. We got Dad home, he was back to normal again, I swear my dad was an iron man of some sort. I would go over to make sure that Dad was taking his meds and doing what the doctors asked him to do.

When I would go over to fix dads meds, all hell broke loose, "Do you not see me in this chair? Do you not see that I need help, what about me?" I told her that if she didn't go easy on me and my father that I was going to remove dad from the house and he could stay with me. She tried to throw something at me, I ducked again she said, "You didn't ask me if I wanted, I wanted to stay." I replied, "You refused to walk and I am not going to cater to your ever need, when you need to start doing some of the things yourself." That broke out into a full-blown cussing out.

This entire time, while I was dealing with my parents, my husband was taking care of his dad. I think we all lived at the hospital. If I wasn't there with my mom, he was there with his dad. The routine for him would be, before work, he would help his dad get dressed and take him downstairs for the day. At night, he would go over and help him up the stairs to get ready for bed.

During this time of caring for parents, our sons were becoming great kids. Growing up in this situation, I believed they handled it very well. My oldest, James was mastering a learning disability, while playing sports, dating. My youngest, Randall was the quiet one; he never wanted any attention brought to him. When his birthday would come around, if you sang Happy Birthday to him, he would run. He too was finding his own in the world of sports. We did the best we could not let much of the family drama take away from them having a happy home. At any cost.

We started to notice that my mom and my husband's dad were just alike in many ways. We would always plan our vacation a year in advance; right before it was time to go, my mom would go to the hospital or his dad would be in there. One year, we were packed, ready to go to the beach. When his sister called, she said, "I don't think you should leave at this moment, Dad is not doing well, I think you should cancel this trip." So, we did. He would go over every day to stay with his dad. Three days into what would have been our vacation, his father died. We are now on our third loss since we have been married.

I was so very sad at the loss of my father-in-law but, again, that part of my mother that was in me was thinking that he would now be able to spend more time with us. Little did I know that would never happen.

My mom fell again, you could see the stress on my dad's face; he was starting to look very tired. While mom was in the hospital, I talked to the social workers, and informed them of how my mother's falling and the constant care was weighing down my father. After talking with my father, they were all in agreement that my mother was better served at a nursing facility.

Of course, I was the one who had to tell her that she will now be living there and not returning home. My ever-living hell returned; she began again that this was all my fault. She went on that I took her leg, her ability to move around and do anything in her house and now I was taking her from her home. I wanted to walk away from her; I wanted to walk away from everything. I wanted to leave her in this hospital room and never look back. *See where you place the blame at.* As I looked at her, with the pain of years gone by, I could only see the pain of my father going forward.

I am an adult now; I don't have to continue to take this shit from her. I did when I was little, but no one says I have to continue it now. I can't stand being blamed for everything that happens to her. I still believe to this very day that I was a problem; the pain of thinking about that keeps coming back. Everything that she did to me and my father growing up, *So you don't want me? I am a problem, then I am out.*

As I was walking out of the door with plans of never seeing her again, I was stopped in my footsteps. I saw my very tired daddy, the same man that protected me when I was little. It was now time for me to do the same for him. I spun around and I told her that she will go to the nursing home and if she wants to come home, then she needs to learn how to walk with her leg and show she can take care of herself, then she would be able to return home.

With that being said, she calmed down, and prepared to go to the nursing home. Six months in, she still hadn't begun to work towards coming home. Her ultimate dreams were coming true; she had all the nurses waiting on her every call. I went over to check on my dad, who had been doing much better since mom was in the home. He would go see her every day at 6:30 and leave at 7:00pm. That seemed to be working well, while I was at the nursing home to hang out with my dad with NO drama, which was great.

We had now gotten my mother settled and used to her new place. I was time to focus on my oldest son. He was hitting a milestone that I couldn't wait to get to when I was his age. He was graduating. This for me was very hard. My son had chosen to go to a school in Ohio. I had enough death in my life, so to me, this felt like he was going away, and I would never see him again. We took our normal vacation to the beach and we all had a great time, until the last day was here. I knew that the following weekend, I would have to let go of my son. Let him become the best version of himself he could be.

When we got to the school, I was holding up well. Then it was time to go; I hugged him tight, fighting back the tears. I didn't want him to worry about me while he was at school. On the way home, we stopped at a gas station for snacks and gas; I went into the restroom, locked the door and cried like someone had died. I fell to the floor of the nasty restroom with my face pressed against the wall. A few minutes had passed, then I came out, to meet my youngest son. He said, "Mom, I could hear you in there are you ok?" "Yes, son I am fine. One of my heartbeats has left the house." My husband was quite all the way back to Virginia.

Back home, I noticed that Dad was moving kind of slow and also having a hard time breathing. I asked him if he was ok. He replied that he had a doctor's appointment and would like for me to go with him. He also said that if I said anything to anyone, he wouldn't tell me anything else. So, I believe that he knows more than what he is telling me. Not the time to get upset, time to stay focused on my buddy and make sure that everything is ok with him.

Little did I know it wasn't; my dad had lung cancer and poor circulation in his left leg and foot. The doctor was not very positive about the outcome; he suggested that my dad go through Chemo treatment, in order to prolong his life a bit. After the first treatment, it was hard for my dad to drive. However, he was persistent that he was going to drive back and forth to wherever he needed to go.

His visits started to slow up with my mother; when I was out to visit, she would ask where he was. She also noticed that he wasn't looking like his self. I explained that with the change in weather his breathing was acting up and he didn't want to get her upset. My mother being her, turns to me and said, you can bring him out here to see me. He doesn't have to drive; you can do it. I, in turn, said to her, "You have got to be crazy; he doesn't feel good and I am not going to make him come out here just to see you; it's not happening."

She pushed the call button for the nurse and asked her to take me out of the room, she no longer wanted me in there because I wasn't doing what she wanted. As I walked out the door, I told her that "One day, you will live to regret treating me and daddy the way you are." To this very day, I think I spoke it into existence. Regarding my dad, as the treatments continued, the after affects would get worse, along with his driving. The doctor told me that I would have to find a way to take the keys from him. Driving was his life line; how could I do this to him?

After dad would get his treatments, I would sit across the parking lot in my car waiting for him to leave so I could follow him home to make sure nothing happened to him. I went over one day to visit my dad, but he was moving really slow. He wasn't up to driving; he asked me to go to the store for him, so I did and got all his snacks that he wanted.

He was trying to vacuum, but I told him I would do it for him; he said he had it and that I should go see my mother and tell her that he was ok. Don't tell her one thing. I responded, "Yes sir." I started heading to the nursing home, but something told me to swing back to the house. I sat outside the house and I could see my dad holding onto the chair trying to clean up. I went into the house and my dad could barely breathe. I told him to "Go rest, I got this."

After seeing this, I asked my brother to increase his visits to dad. Dad wouldn't suspect anything out of my brother showing up often, like he would me. My brother said he would. December time has come and my dad loved to put lights outside on his porch; this year, I told him "I was so into the holidays right now, let me do it and you tell me where you want them." We had fun doing that together.

My brother drove him down to see my Grandmother; she noticed that something was wrong with him; after their visit, I told my brother and my Grandmother what was going on and he had me keep this a secret for a good 6 months. He had told me that if I told anyone, he wouldn't let me go to his appointments and we needed to know what was going on. I am not the over-the-top church going person, but I do believe. I prayed and asked God "Could my dad please make it through the holidays, it is not in my control," but I didn't want him to die at all. However, I didn't want him to pass on Christmas or Christmas Eve, it is my brother's birthday and no one wants a love one to die on their birthday. Thankfully, Christmas was fun. We all spent a lot of time laughing and just having a good time. I tried to get my mom to join us at Daddy's house, but she refused to leave.

We all went out to visit my mother; she was in her feelings that no one came out to see her before 2:00pm. I told her that we had to visit like we always did, so she shouldn't be upset like this. There are people in here with her that have no one visit them. For once, could she be grateful in her life? I walked out and after cooling down, I went back in the room. She was laughing and having a good time with everyone else. When I came in, she got quiet. UGH! This is getting old; for Dad, I will stay strong.

Saturday after Christmas, it was chores as usual. I went over to Dad's to get his grocery list. I didn't see him in his room or watching TV. I headed to the kitchen, no dad; I looked to my left, there was my dad lying on the bathroom floor. I started to lose it, but I knew I had to check to make sure he was still alive. Once I saw that he was still breathing, he said to leave him there, he was going to be ok. I called my husband and asked him to leave work, explaining that my dad was on the floor. He got there to help him and had to pull my poor daddy's pants up to put him back in the chair. While he was doing that, I had called 911; they had gotten to the house just as we got Daddy in the chair. 911 said he needed to go to the hospital. I was right behind them.

If you thought taking my Grandmother off life support was hard, that was nothing compared to the ton of bricks that was getting ready to be dropped on me. The doctor pulled me out to tell me there's nothing they can do; they are going to make him comfortable, but at the rate this was going, it should be a few days if that long. My brother showed up and just crumbled in his chest. I told my brother what the doctor said; now we all have to go into the room to tell Daddy. As the doctor was telling him, my dad said, "If it is my time to go, I am in a good place; my daughter has everything under control." My heart broke with each word.

I stayed with my daddy that night; I wanted to be there when he died. The following night was my brother's turn. He went to get my Grandmother so that she could see him that Sunday morning. We all were shocked dad was up; he was eating and told my Grandmother that he would be down next Sunday to take care of the bills. Everyone was so upbeat about this I stayed with dad and he started to sleep; he wouldn't wake up to eat and the doctor told me we didn't have much time. I asked what happened, since he was just up. He explained the stages of transition; my dad was doing them all.

I didn't sleep at all that night. I would doze off, but I just watched him, saying to myself, *how could the man that protected me all of my life, the strongest man I know, be laying here ready to take his last breath?* Morning came and he seemed to have stalled breathing. Mid-morning, he took one deep breath, then he was gone. Just like that, December 29th, my world was gone, broken and spinning. I pushed the button for the nurse to let them know that he was gone. I had to call the family so they could see him before they took him away.

We had to go and tell my mom. At first, she was upset; we did what we could to console her, but it was like a switch flipped. "Who is going to take care of me?" I was angry that she was even thinking about this; I had to remember what had just happened, maybe she is not clear at this moment. I replied, "I will be handling your affairs, and everything that daddy was doing, you need not worry about yourself at this time."

The day of service for Daddy, was the hardest thing I ever had to get ready for. My thoughts went to the times he would take me to my Grandmother; how he protected me from my mom and her issues. How he threatened me to walk down the aisle, it was me and him riding this out to the end. My ride with my Daddy ended just like it started, protection, the unexpected and love. Many people showed up to the service. When the service was starting, I asked to close his casket. I know that he couldn't see me, but I wanted to be the last one he saw. I also put his favorite hat in the casket with him, so that he would be able to wear it when he got to heaven. On the program, I had put my brother and myself to speak. My brother explained to me that is something that he didn't want to do. At this point, I really didn't care what he wanted to do, I need to make sure that Daddy's home-going was the best it could be. I told happy stories about my dad; that hat he never went anywhere without it. The plan was to keep the good memories, not that he wasn't with us anymore.

At the graveside, the military was there to play taps. Dad served in the Army; that was the hardest thing to hear, and then they gave me the flag off his coffin. That's when I finally started to cry. When the service was completed, they wanted to lower him in the ground, but was waiting for me to leave. I responded that "I am not going anywhere until this is completed." My brother came up the hill and asked if I was going back to the church, I said, "Yes, but not until I see this through." His response was, "Suit yourself." He walked away and returned to the church to fill his stomach and socialize.

As the months went by, my mother started to become a handful for me. She refused to come out of her room and refused any medical assistance. We had to get a mental evaluation, which came back that she was having memory loss and signs of being aggressive. Without the alcohol, she was returning to her old ways and that scared me, even as an adult. I can't believe as a full-grown adult, the drama that I lived throughout my childhood was coming back. She was hateful, rude and sometimes threatening. I would repeat in my head *if dad could do it, then so can I.* That was a blow, but nothing like what I was going to hear when I got home.

I was so exhausted when I got home. My husband called me into the kitchen and the look on his face was not a good one. I was saying to myself, *what in the world is wrong now?* He told me the last three months he had been keeping something from me. He said he didn't want to say anything until he had all the information.

He has prostate cancer, and we are going to be in the fight of our lives. He didn't want to tell me since I was so fresh off dealing with my dad's death due to cancer. Now we have to tell the kids; James had moved back from Ohio, and was a manager at a big box store. I knew exactly what they were going to feel, my heart was breaking for them. When we told them, there were no tears in front of them. We didn't want to scare them with the thought of death, especially, when it was Randall's last year of high school.

My husband made the largest request, one of the hardest requests he could have ever made. I couldn't tell anyone. What? How was I supposed to get through this without some type of support for myself? I can't be your support, your go to and I have no one. As we went on with treatment, he understood what I was saying, so he was ok with his niece knowing because they were really close, and I took it upon myself to tell a few people because I needed that help.

On another note, the calls were coming non-stop regarding my mother. She was not letting the nurses give her a bath and complaining about how bad the food was. She would order something different and still wouldn't eat it. I am not sure what I was thinking by getting her a cell phone; she would call me anytime of the night. One night, she called and said that she was laying on the floor and no one would come pick her up off the floor. I hopped in my car and drove like a fool to get there; she was asleep in the bed. The nurses thought I was crazy for showing up in the middle of the night. She said she didn't call, not knowing we could see the last call going out.

A few days later, I stopped in to see her and I could hear her complaining, being nasty all the way up the hall. When I got to the room, she looked at me and told me that I could get the hell out. She continued that I was just like my dad and she didn't want to see my face. WHAT!? How dare you put my daddy's name in your mouth when he did nothing but take care of you and stayed with you when he should've left you? I ran out of the room and told the nurses to pray I come back. Along with taking care of my mother, my dad left me with the complete care of my Little Granny. So, like we did when I was growing up, every Sunday, we were down there to check on her, pay bills and fix anything that needed work.

While all of this was going on, Mom was starting to get ill and sick more often, where she would have to make trips to the hospital. My husband was also getting more aggressive treatments. His last few visits, his Prostrate numbers were going up and not coming down. The doctors were determined to fight this and win. I was happy with the efforts that they were making to save a life.

One day during the month of August, the phone rang. They were taking my mom to the hospital; she was talking out of her head, not making sense. When I got there, the doctor told me that she was retaining a lot of fluid. They were going to do the best that they could to help her, but her heart was not pumping fast enough to move the fluid from her heart. Again, I heard, "We are going to make her comfortable, she may have a week to live." This was at the end of August.

Remember I was born September 27th. This was my 50th birthday, a milestone that everyone looks forward to, I was no different from the rest. I had planned a paint party with the girls on the 24th. I know I was wrong for saying this, but once my mom made it into September, I told my husband that "I feel deep in my bones that my mother is going to have the last say and her spot in the light. She is going to die on the day of the party or my birthday." He said "Don't say that." I reminded him, "Do you not remember the woman that only wanted you to talk to her and not anyone around her?"

"She would get angry if you did talk to anyone but her. Do you remember me sharing my childhood with you? How she treated my dad the entire time they were married? Why wouldn't she do this?" No one believed me. I told Elise, my friend of 30 plus years, this is what I believed in my heart was going to happen. She too said she didn't believe me. I said, "Ok, watch and see."

We made it to my birthday party on the 24th. I had an amazing time. I took her cake and some of the food from the party. She had enough energy to say that she didn't want that mess. "Order me wings from the pizza place." I wanted to say something, but I had to channel my daddy, reminding myself over and over again that if he could do it, so could I. I responded to her with a, "Yes, I would be more than happy to." I placed the order and the food arrived. She said it was nasty and she didn't want it. I left the room angry and I told the nurses I needed to go calm down.

A few days had gone by and the nurses called to say that my mother was having labored breathing and was asking for me. I went back the next day; she was in and out of it, but while I was there, she was the mother that I always wanted. We laughed and joked around, then she said something that will always stay with me. "Happy Birthday." I said, "My birthday is tomorrow, you can tell me then." She looked at me and said, "Sure. We left on a good note."

6:00am, September 27th, the next morning, the phone rings and my mom had died on my 50th birthday. As wrong as it may sound, I was sad, but at the same time, relieved. 50 years of verbal abuse, alcohol, unnecessary beatings and sometimes good times, but not as many as the bad, had come to an end.

I held her service at the funeral home; it was short and to the point. Her nieces and nephews were there to speak on how they are going to miss her and all she had done for them. I looked at one point to make sure she was talking about the same person. Just like Dad, I put pens, and search puzzles in her casket. Those were her favorite things. She would always take your pen and always wanted a new book and snacks she wasn't supposed to have because she was a diabetic

I was in charge of handling my mothers' affairs just like I was my father's. I needed to get a birth certificate for my mother in order to complete some of the needed things to close the chapter on my 50 plus years of hell. In the mail came the paperwork needed; I opened it and was crushed.

It listed her mother and her father, but my grandfather as I knew him to be until the day he died, was NOT! My mother's father. Listed on the paperwork, it said that the person I thought was my uncle until the day he died, was her father. My Big Granny was not her mother either. I kind of thought she wasn't, because my mom would talk about her sister and brother who lived down the street. So as a kid, you didn't think about it. You just knew you had a large family on my mother's side.

I called my brother on the phone; his response was, "Yeah, that's correct." "What the Hell you mean that is correct?" He said, "Pooh there are a lot of things that went on that you didn't know about that they wanted to keep from you, just to keep you protected."

Then my wheels started; I was getting angrier with each thought. I said to my brother, "We have a brother that no one is telling me who the father is, how did this happen?" Now I am sounding this out with my brother, "we have the only reason Mom and Dad got married was because she was pregnant with you. Now I have, my grandfather was nothing but a stranger that used to look after me."

My next question, "Was my daddy my real daddy or not? Don't lie to me like everyone else." The phone went silent, and he said, "Yes, daddy was your daddy." I thought I was done with the lies, and all the hidden secrets, when that crap about the brother that's a cousin, my mother giving him to her sister to raise- came up. That information about Klein was taken to the grave. No one ever told me the truth. This is one crazy ass family.

I knew that this was going to be a lot on my youngest, to try to finish school, prepare for college and know that your father could be dying. I broke his request, not to tell anyone he was sick. I reached out to Randall's football coach and basketball coach, who was just like a member of the family, and the school counselors. I wanted him to have someone he could go to if he needed anything.

During one of the football games, he was catching a pass in the end zone for a touchdown and he was pushed into the goal post

This resulted in a concussion, which had him out of school for 32 days. His high school was the best. They did all they could to make sure he got caught up so that he could return to basketball and graduate.

As graduation approached, my husband still had not informed his workplace of his illness. "We are two years into this battle, and all they know is you have doctors' appointments? I know that they have to know something's going on. You are out of breath when you are walking, you are starting to look thin."

Graduation night finally arrived; my last heartbeat was getting ready to walk across the stage. He showed up, looks very tired and worn out, but he was still there. When my youngest boy's name was called, my shy child danced across the stage. I don't think his family could have been prouder. I looked to my left and smiled at his brother, because I was so very proud of him also.

Here I was, thinking I was heading into new beginnings; we could focus on our family and taking care of my Little Granny. That seemed not to be. As we continued his battle with cancer, they had changed over to a more aggressive treatment for him, by installing a port under his skin for his chemo treatment.

He started to plan our annual trip to South Carolina for the summer. This summer will be different. Randall will attend college this year.

With the progression of the cancer, I asked my husband if he was up for it; he said no, but he wanted to see the beach for possibly the last time. Our trip was here upon us. I was so looking forward to going and relaxing from all that had gone on in the past year. Our room had a great view of the beach, so he could sit on the deck; he couldn't go into the water anymore, because he had a bag attached to him to so he could go to the bathroom without accidents.

This trip was one that I wanted to be over soon. Randall, had never seen his father when he was not feeling good; there were mood swings came with it. We went out to breakfast and there was an issue with the food, so I was working to get it taken care of. My husband came back in the store and snapped at me as to what was taking so long? I was hurt and embarrassed that he would do that. When I was driving back to the hotel, my son could see that I was about to cry. He was getting upset; when we arrived at the hotel, he slammed the door and went to the room.

My son and I walked slowly and I was trying to explain to him that it's cancer making him do that and its' ok. He turned to me and said, "It's not ok. You went through years of this with Nana; you are not going to do it again with him." I said, "He has been like this since the treatments started. We had a few days left to go on our trip and I wanted to do a dinner cruise at sunset and he wanted to go fishing. I said to myself that *this could be his last trip, let's do what he wanted.*

I brought food with us; this was the compromise. I had never gone fishing before, so this was going to be interesting. Guess who caught more fish? Yup you got it, this girl. I had more fun than I thought I would. I was hoping that this would put him in a good mood. Nope, he started in on my son, because he wasn't going out on the beach. I said, "That is not his thing; if he doesn't want to be in the sand, then leave him be, this is his trip as much as yours."

When we returned, it was the hardest thing I had to prepare for. My baby was leaving the house to go off to school. He was going to be two hours away; we dropped him off, and on the way back home, I was getting messages that he wanted us to come back and get him. The school was not a good fit for him. I reached out to the football coach to see if he could help us with getting him settled.

Once we got home, my husband said that he was not going to have him in a place he is not comfortable; Randall was upset and he asked to send him a message that his dad would be there in the morning to pick him up. Little did we know that all things happen for a reason. When he returned home, he helped his dad out with painting his aunt's house, due to his dad slowing down, but he refused to stop. My heart sank, as I watched my husband lean against the tree. This was the same lean my dad started to do, towards the end.

I was at work and my phone rang. It was the doctor's office. I had made a deal with them that if they were ever to give him a timeline, I needed to know first. That was the call; the doctor said that his numbers had doubled in a week. There wasn't anything they could do for him, but keep him comfortable. All I could say was, "Here I go again."

I called his niece to tell her that they are going to give him a timeline. The morning of the appointment, he started to not feel well and they thought he was having a heart attack, so they brought him into the office. His niece was 20 minutes out. I asked them to wait for her to get here and they did. While we were waiting, they had started prepping him; when the doctors said that his numbers had doubled in a week, my husband asked, "How much time do I have?"

I nodded my head. It was time to tell him. You have 3 months if not 5 months. He started to cry, then I lost it. He said that he had to get to an appointment on Monday; I told him "Don't worry about that, we will get there. I will take the days off needed to get things set up." The doctor said that we will have the cancer support group come out tomorrow to get you all set up. When his niece got there, she was destroyed by the news. We went over to the hospital to make sure that he didn't have a heart attack.

After he was clear, we got home and he laid down on the sofa where he stayed. The next day, hospice support came in. When I told her that he was starting his transition, she looked at me and said, "There is no way he could be going into that. He was just told how he had a good 3 months." I, in turn, said "Look and you will see, I have gone through these three times before, I recognized the signs." As she continued to work on him, she turned to me, "You are right."

At that moment, I knew I had to get ready to be the rock for the kids. Thursday night, I was able to get him up to the bathroom but he no longer wanted food. Every time I would get out of his sight, he would call for me. I was trying to get the house ready for the items the nurse said would be coming over.

I had cleared the back bedroom, to prepare for the hospital bed so that we could get him in the bed. I heard a knock on the door; there stood my friend, Elise. I was happy to see her because I was not prepared to do this. They asked me why I didn't send him to the hospital, but I made a promise to him that I would make sure he died in his home. So, this was what we were going to do. Elise tried her best not to laugh, but whenever I would walk out of the room, he would call me.

Soon, the hospital bed came. Elise and my son help my husband off the sofa. We got him in the bed, I looked at the nurse and I said, "How much time?" She responded, "Through the weekend if we are lucky." I got on the phone to reach out to his family. I let his oldest sister take care of the rest of the family to let them know they need to get here as soon as possible.

I went in to check on him, with my husband's brother, I told him, "You can talk to him, he can hear you." He was always worried that he wouldn't get the house for his sister completed before something happened to him. When his eyes opened, I told him

"Your brother is here, he wanted you to know that everything in the house is complete, so you don't have to worry about it." I know I lied to him but you have to do what you have to do.

After he heard that, the nurse and my friend came in. I noticed that his breathing was starting to slow down. I sat beside him and told him he was the greatest father, son, brother and husband he could be. He took a deep breath and he was gone. September 17th, not a complete year had gone by since my mother's death, here I sat with a husband, who is now dead.

His sister and brother didn't make it back in time to talk to him while he was alive. One sister just lost it, which didn't help my kids, who were trying to understand and process that their father was no longer here. The funeral home came and the family cleared the room. I was in the kitchen with guests and family when they brought him through. I made them stop. Why? I don't know. I opened the body bag to make sure it was him, and that's when it really hit me.

I started to cry so hard. I have no idea to this day why I was or the floor and how I got there. I do remember that someone was giving me shots of Tequila, to take the edge off. I slowly returned to myself, to never have another outburst like that again.

We had talked about him being cremated; my plan was to honor that request. His family on the other hand was upset that I would burn their brother. I saw this was going to be the start of a big fight. His niece was my biggest support when it came to the service; my friend of 30 years handled the house.

The church was packed with family and friends. Like the other services that I had, I stood up and spoke. That too was the topic of discussion. How could you do that? Where did you find the strength to speak as your husband lay in front of you? Other topic of discussion, after the services, we were going to my house or so I thought.

We were raised in such a way that after funerals, you are supposed to go to the home of the deceased. That didn't happen in this case. Most of the family on his side went to his sister's house, to spend time together. The only person that came to the house was my nephew. His niece went home and she wasn't feeling well; his other sister went home also. She had all of the family she could take. No phone calls from them or anything. I figured out from the gossip after the service, that they were upset with me because I didn't tell them anything about his illness, the fact that we had been fighting it for 2 years, and I didn't tell anyone. As I said before, it wasn't my story to tell. He told who he wanted to know; I respected his wishes.

Once everything calmed down, I sat in my house and looked around. I was alone, now what do I do with my life? I am no longer a grand-daughter, a daughter or a wife. I can now live the life that I have always wanted, or thought I would have.

How It Came to Be

I hope that reading my story will give you the courage to know you can overcome anything. Stay strong, keep pushing and know that any drama you are facing will go away.

This book started off as a way to vent about the treatment of my past. I got into expressing my feelings, I thought to myself, *I know there are others out there that could have started off in life in this manner. Could I reach one person to let them know that you can get away? You can break the mold; you don't have to follow in your parents' footsteps and become that person.*

It's never too late to follow your dreams. I thought that my life would take me down a path of destruction. I did it all; alcohol, drugs, fighting. I found a way out, a new way to look at life, to live life. To help kids along the way know that no matter how bad life is at home, reach deep down inside of you, find that strength to pull through.

Know that every storm that you go through will end with a rainbow. I am proof of that.

ACKNOWLEDGMENTS

I WANT TO THANK MY FAMILY, loved ones, and friends who stood with me from the start to completing my book.

To my sons, Eric and Evan Coleman, you were there through thick and thin. We have seen the lowest of lows and highest of highs. We are still here, standing strong.

To Law Lewis, you reminded me to never give up on myself. When things are going rough, there will always be a brighter side. You also reminded me to love myself, and all else will fall into place.

To Jennifer Timms, when I wanted to stop writing, your

support and encouragement helped me to the finish line.

And to Deidra Hughes, Deshanta Starks Turner, Jennifer Grazler, Brandon Williams, and Marilyn Whiting, thank you for being a constant ear, shoulder, and true friends.

Thank you for supporting my vision:

- J.F. Bell Funeral Home 108 Sixth ST NW Charlottesville, VA 22902
- Law Logistics Richmond VA, Email-lawlogistics@gmail.com
- Taste of Tee 1118 Preston Ave Charlottesville, VA 22902 terrencesmith786@gmail.com 434-422-1287

Pamela James Coleman

ABOUT THE AUTHOR

BORN TO ALFRED AND SHIRLEY JAMES, Pamela James Coleman was raised in Charlottesville, Virginia. Colman attended elementary, middle, and high school in Charlottesville, VA, and she also attended Virginia State University, located in Petersburg, VA. Coleman has an older brother, Alfred James, Jr, and she also has two sons, Eric and Evan Coleman, and grandson Maverick Coleman whom she loves all dearly.

Getting into the professional side of life, Coleman is a teacher's assistant for special needs children in elementary school, and she is launched a website, "Web N Today." This website will assist many with handling their social media websites.

In addition, Coleman loves taking scenic photos. She will stop on the side of the road if something catches her eye. Coleman is down for shopping any minute of the hour, but what may come as a shocker is her love for the Washington Football Team. If you ever want to debate, she's up for the task, but it doesn't stop there. Coleman is a Nascar racing fan and has been for the last 15 years. Not only does she have a friend who's a Nascar driver, but she has met at least 20 drivers.

You never really live life until you take action and do

something you're passionate about, and Coleman has done that and more. Coleman has a passion for volunteering to help local groups. Two of those groups include the Victory Junction Camp for kids with disabilities in North Carolina and the Women's Four Miler, a breast cancer center in Virginia, where her mission is to raise funds. Coleman's hobbies and passions have led her to fulfill her dream to share her life story from beginning to present. She has added the career of a future best-selling author who's a part of the Embracing Her-Story community of authors with SHE PUBLISHING LLC to her resume.

For those who know Coleman on a more personal level, they would confess that she always put others before herself, gives her last to help someone else, likes creating laughter, and offers 100% on any tasks she takes on, even if it means she has to work over-time to get it done. In short, Coleman enjoys being personable. She tries to mail cards to friends and family once a month instead of a simple text message or phone call; Coleman loves to travel, attend sporting events, and she has never met a cake that she didn't like.

Welcome to the world of

PAMELA JAMES COLEMAN

Is this me? Am I her?

CPSIA information can be obtained
at www.ICGtesting.com
Printed in the USA
BVHW072056251121
622403BV00001B/28

9 781953 163322